ANATOMY OF A BROKEN HEART

O.O.Kukoyi

For Matcelle Antie,

Looking Forward to reading your
life's story

Special thanks to Abe, Enoima, Sam, Jay, Uzor, Toju, Jessica, and Osas; you're all made of the same stuff as miracles.

What is it in storms that somehow guide us home?

CONTENTS

JOHN

They all sat on the sand, quietly looking through one another:
seeing only pieces of the broken people they had now become.
There is no comfort in shared pain. It hurts so much more
when those you love mourn too - that empty whole you all feel
slowly becomes far greater than the sum of all the happiness
you've ever shared.

This is how the forest feels when winter claims its first leaf.
John was the first of them to die, and he was the best of them.
One moment he was laughing, the next, he was being washed
ashore: rejected by the same sea that claimed his life.

Metaphors and Similitudes.

Leftover pasta usually tastes better the next day, but not today. This tastes like shit. I tossed the bowl filled with fusilli on the breakfast table, ignored the pile of dirty plates I had been collecting for a while now, and reluctantly dragged my feet as I made my way to the fridge. I reached for the jug of milk, took a huge gulp, and immediately spat it out. It was way past stale.

My phone vibrates. Lately, it's been my most reliable source of bad news; it's a reminder for the train ticket I just bought 15 minutes ago. "Your train departs Manchester Piccadilly in 45 minutes." The train station is just a 6-minute drive from me. Let me head down to the office for a minute or two.

...

"A train cabin is a strange place to meet God," he said, as he sat across from me on the train. He webbed his fingers together and put his hands on the table. Then looked at me, or maybe through me, I honestly couldn't tell.

I felt a strange kind of uncomfortable- the kind that seemed more welcome than unnerving; somehow it felt okay if he could see through me, and know what my thoughts were. Someone needed to.

I had no intention of talking to the strange man on the train, so I just smiled and nodded in response to his rather awkward statement. I'm not sure he got the gist because he continued to speak anyways.

"Am I on the wrong train?" He asked me calmly.
"I think I'm on the wrong train," he said to himself after I refused to reply.

"I have no idea who you are, or where you're going, but If you're this confused about it, then you're definitely on the wrong train," I thought to myself- finding some humour in what looked like his careless misfortune. Maybe someone could be headed to a worse day than I was having. My tiny spurt of joy faded when I realised that even though he might have been having a bad day, he couldn't possibly have been having bad days so consistently it led to worst 9 months of his life. That reality was just mine alone to live.

That Saturday morning, I had just received a mail from that last member of my start-up team, telling me he was leaving as well. 5 other people had quit already. "The business isn't working," he wrote, "and I'm out." How impassioned and precise.

That was the last straw that broke me. It had been an excruciating 9 months of disappointing sales, shattered expectations, and unreliable investors. I blamed everything from the design of my website to the city I was living and working in. I had called my only mentor to know if I could come see him in London, and to tell him I was thinking of quitting or moving, or both. I was in a bad place in life generally. I slept a lot these days. Sleep is a place I go to very often when I hate consciousness; it's the place I go to contemplate the important things in life like giving up or suicide.

I turned my focus back at the man to find out he never stopped looking at me. I noticed his eyes; he had honest hazel eyes - they were full of truth, like the eyes you'd see in the face of a baby. There was an ease about him, I didn't like it, but I wanted some of it.

"It always takes a void to create a universe, Sean. Have you considered that the things you lack are God's tool for your abundance?" He said while looking straight into my eyes.

"What?

3

I haven't told you my name, have I?
I didn't say my name, did I?" I asked myself.

"How do you know my name?" I asked loudly, distracting the other passengers on the train.

He said nothing. He just kept looking at me, or through me, I still couldn't tell.

It freaked me out. But I wasn't going to let him know that. In fact, what freaked me out the most was that somehow it didn't freak me out, and somehow it really did. That's what was most upsetting.

I still wasn't interested in having a conversation; I just wanted to sleep, as I always did whenever I started to feel depressed. So I made up my mind to pay no more attention to the strange man whose complete attention seemed to be fixed on me. "It's the UK; people are strange," I thought to myself. I closed my eyes and started to drift into sleep; into the unconsciousness that always numbed my disdain for my own life.

I wasn't fully asleep yet. I was at that edge right before you fall deeply into sleep- where your mind is somehow conscious of the whole world, but your body is somewhat sedated. I could hear the baby crying several seats from mine, and I knew why the teenagers in the other cabin were laughing. I understood the couple who were having a bit of a ruckus in Spanish completely, though I knew nothing of the language.

"Sean!"
He called to me with the audacity in a thunderclap.

I opened my eyes, and I was wide awake, and back in my office. Sitting at my desk thinking "Gosh I'm going to miss my train."

4

The office looked different. All of my things had been packed up; my hopes, dreams, and files were now in boxes. I was moving out, apparently because the business had failed. But the strange man on the train was there with me. "How is he here? He is much taller than I remember, come to think of it, I never saw him standing in my dream. How is he here?"

He was now dressed, in a navy pinstriped double-breasted suit that looked like it was sewn in a place where all was right with the world. He stood at the window with both hands in his pockets looking at the trees as they danced in the wind. It was raining outside. It rarely rained this hard in Manchester. It drizzles so often that whenever it rained hard, it felt like the end of the world. But in this room right now looking at all these boxes, for me, it was the end of the world- it was the end of my world.

"Who are you and why are-"

"Listen to silence! And you might just hear the voice of God." He said as he cut me off with the same authority with which he had called me from my dream.

"Are you God?"
I asked forcefully as I got up from my chair, totally ignoring the "shut-up" he had just said so profoundly.

He let a very long silence ensue. I can't tell you how long. It was an eternity, and it wasn't. Ever so often he'd hum a familiar tune as if to serenade the dancing trees outside my window. I think it was more to calm my raging seas.

"There are no coincidences in life, just independent incidents and random people connected by a greater purpose. I am that greater purpose that makes coincidences happen, I am the will that's far greater than yours, and I am the reason that connects

all things. No, I'm not God, but we are very very close-
inseparable even. So yes I am God."

It was weird; sometimes he neither said yes nor no. At times he
always said both yes and no, but I understood everything
without question. Who he was wasn't important: it was what he
was that was important. What he was held the answer to why he
was here with me in my office, right now. I could see clearly
how the name of a thing isn't as important as the purpose of a
thing. Standing beside him, I could understand everything.

"The height of a tree matters less than its strength against
raging winds, don't you think?" He said as he took a longing
look at the trees, turned around and walked towards the exit of
the office complex. I followed him. He didn't seem the slightest
bit bothered about the pouring rain, or getting his well-tailored
suit drenched. He just walked to the exit and opened the door.

We stepped out into a great forest path with a balustrade of
trees on either side. The trees had fallen in love eons ago and
were now holding hands several feet above our heads. Their
affection shielded us from the sun which honestly, felt
friendlier than it should, considering how bright the path was.

"The path less travelled births a lonely walk, and a man
without a guide may lose his way. Remind me again Sean, how
you met the man who is now your mentor, and friend."

"Oh, it was luck really. I was at the right place at the right
time. His son spilled his drink: they poured on my shoes.
That's how we got talking."

"Hmmm, a coincidence."

He didn't speak for a while, and we didn't walk either. We just
stood in the middle of the path, and I gloried in the beauty of
it all.

"That office we just left behind is everything you ever feared, isn't it? All your dreams and hard work packed up in boxes, - the empty spaces they leave behind screaming out to everyone that you've failed.

"Yes, it is."

"I've seen how sometimes the path of the righteous leads through the valley of the shadow of death. But I've also seen how the valley of the shadow of death leads to the river of life, Sean."

"That reminds me of a story I used to hear at Sunday school as a child." I said. "That's the story of David, right?" I asked, completely interrupting him.

He wasn't fazed by my interruption; he knew the things I had to say before I did. As a matter of fact, I think every time I spoke I was saying the less profound parts of his thoughts; leaving him to say the parts that really mattered.

"Stories are powerful things," he continued, - "they are metaphors and similitudes that guide the living- the tales you hear are the tales you tell. I know the story of every soul that has ever walked the face of the earth. I've met some of them in person like I'm meeting you now; I've seen them when they were filled with life, and when they were close to death. I've spoken to them in their good times and in their bad- and every one of those who made it through the bad are those who held on to the very same hope they had when all was good."

We were now in a field of flowers. Don't ask me how we got there; I have no idea. He stopped to look at the flowers with the same passion he had in his eyes when he looked at the trees. He seemed to love nature deeply like he knew a secret about her that none of us would ever know in 16 lifetimes.

"Hope is a rose tossed by the wind. Fragile as it is, it still never breaks. It's the fire that keeps burning in your heart when everything else is gone. It's a fire you light long before you try to walk in the dark."

"You hope for the best long before you see the worst, and long after you do," I thought to myself...

Before I could finish my thought, he turned around as if distracted by something in the distance, I turned around as well to see what he was looking for, only to find myself sitting at my desk in the office, everything unpacked and it's rightful place.
He sat across my desk in front of me. He had a different look in his eye now, I think it was hope, I think he saw a little bit of hope in me. He looked at me for a while with a smile on his face, and then he continued to talk.

"Time requires that everything changes, yet remains the same; that old tales birth new adventures; that aged trees birth new fruits; that old men dream new dreams.

Things are seldom as they seem, Sean. A cold winter kills off leaves but preserves the soil, a hot summer greens the trees but scorches the earth- the very same thing that brings death to the caterpillar brings life to the butterfly... It always takes a void to create a universe! Maybe the things you lack are God's tools for all of your abundance.

Not all the verses of a great book are quotable. Not all the days of your great life will be memorable. Deal with it, Sean, never lose hope."

I felt four strong taps on my shoulder. It wasn't the strange man tapping me; I could still see him sat right in front of me. I looked up to see who it was - and it's the train master. "What's he doing here?" I thought.

I looked back to the place where the strange man was sat half a moment ago- it's an empty chair in an empty train cabin!

"Sir, where are you headed to?" The train master asked.

"Where is the man that was sitting there?" I asked, ignoring his question, frantically pointing to the seat right opposite mine.

"I think you fell asleep on your trip from Manchester. If there was anyone sat there, he's probably left now. We've been in London for the past seven minutes," he said while looking at his watch. "I am cleaning up the train, preparing for our return trip to Manchester, so if you're not going that way, you should probably get off now. The passengers headed toward Manchester are about to come on."

I ran out of the train in a frenzy and stood on the platform confused, wondering what the hell kind of dream that was.

Something Celestial

The first conversation we ever had was at the worst of times. She had just lost her brother; I had just failed at my most recent attempt at success. Yet, our two broken hearts mended into an unlikely friendship, an unlikely friendship we nurtured into a great love[1].

Hers was a life of oysters and champagne; mine was riddled with unfinished manuscripts and broken dreams; still, we loved each other faultlessly, like the earth loved the sea. Our love wasn't the kind that burned so hot it seared hearts. It was the cold unassuming kind; the kind we don't see in movies; the kind that said 'thank you' for absolutely no reason; the kind that celebrated silly anniversaries lying in bed all day, holding each other- becoming each other.

I remember seeing her for the first time at a house party a few months before we ever spoke, catching her eye and immediately looking away. I had to; her eyes were the closest I had ever been to the sun. Everyone flocked around her seeking warmth from something celestial. To me, she was everything that explained the reason behind the Big Bang. I think she knew that hers was a cosmic kind of beauty; she wore the Milky-way as shoes: Supernovas, Blackholes, and Neutron stars leathered around her feet. I thought it rather fitting because somewhere within her I knew there was a universe I belonged to; somewhere within her was a void my evolution was designed to fill.

Then came two months of unanswered friend requests, unrequited Facebook pokes and ignored Instagram direct messages. I had built rocket ships to get five feet closer to her, but crashed and burned and never kissed her orbit.

---

[1] See cover Art

I all but gave up until I saw her walking towards me on a train platform, headed to the same city I had just sworn to leave behind. A coincidence I'd never forget.

A KIND OF REGRET.

"Second thoughts are useless when making first impressions."
That's what I thought as I walked towards her window seat on
the train from London Euston to Manchester Piccadilly. I've
not exactly been known for my courage in these situations, but
it's never courage that draws a moth to the flame. There was
something different about her today. Much of her grace, it
seemed, had been veiled behind a heavy frown. I sat next to her
- sitting across from her would be too much of a risk. The less
of those eyes I saw right now, the better for my nerves. It
wasn't until I sat next to her that I noticed her infallible skin -
she had the kind of sweet caramel complexion that shamelessly
celebrates love bites and hickeys.

"Hi," I said confidently. Knowing fully well that was all the
"Hi" I could muster for this two-hour trip, and if she chose not
to respond, I'd just pretend to be really busy doing something
important the rest of the journey.

"Hi, are you one of John's friends?" she asked cautiously, but
expectantly.

"Aargh, no," I replied. Thankful, but more nervous now that
she answered...

"Well, I feel like we've met before." She said, her eyes
desperately searching her mind for the answer.

"I wouldn't say we've met, I saw you at that party at the
Gbolade's a few months ago."

She thought about the party for a moment and began to recluse
into herself again. You see her brother[2] had drowned two days
after that party, but I didn't know that then.

---

[2] John. Pg. 1

'Who's John?" I continued carelessly.

She attempted a reply, then paused; tightening her lips as her eyelids became the dam that held back an overflow.

"John was, is my twin brother."

The dam fails...

Consoling someone you love is hard, but consoling someone you want to love; that's new territory altogether. I had no idea what to say or do. I just sat there looking as she sobbed.

"Didn't you know John?" She asked still in the midst of her tears." He was my brother, and he drowned at a beach a few days after that party. "

Suddenly all my nerves didn't seem to matter anymore- I just wanted her pain to stop. But I knew it wouldn't. I had lost too much myself to know that you that when you lose a friend, or a brother, or a business, the pain never goes away. You feel it every day. It disintegrates into a kind of regret that never leaves you.

"It still hurts so much,-" she continued.

"Maybe it's meant to hurt." I cautiously interrupted... "Maybe the pain we feel when we lose a loved one is how we know they are still reaching out to touch us, and love us, and feel us. Maybe we're are not wired to ever stop feeling that pain, because when we do, it's proof we are truly beyond their reach; maybe that's when they really die."

It took a while, but she finally looked back up, drying her eyes with the sleeves of her black cashmere sweater.

"I just got back from his burial in Abuja, and I'm headed to the flat we share in Manchester. It's the first time we've ever really been apart, and it's forever.
I wasn't prepared for this."

I sighed and said nothing. There is a kind of pain you never try to comfort with words. We both just sat there.

She gathered up herself and broke the silence. "Why were you at the party, I mean, how do you know the Gbolades?"

"Oh, my folks are old family friends with them. They all went to medical school together" I replied.

"Oh okay..." She said, expectant I'd keep the conversation going. I didn't, I didn't know how to.

And another silence ensued... One she soon broke again,

"I'm sorry, I'm usually very good with new people; don't know why I'm bad at it right now."

"Really? I couldn't tell, maybe because I'm terrible at it," I said, careful not to remind her that why she was bad at it was because she was mourning.

She casts half a smile my way and says;
"Tell you what, ask me anything, I don't mean the usual stuff like where I schooled, or where I work; just ask something you think you'd really want to know about me, and I'd answer."

"You sure?" I asked.

"Yeah!" She responded, almost immediately, like an ember that had been longing for the wind that rekindles fire.

"Okay then..."

I thought for a minute asking myself what it was I found most curious about the girl on the train. And it came.

"Tell me about your first heartbreak." I said with a smile on my face, rather impressed by my own question.

"Really, that's the first thing want to ask, after I just sobbed all over you?"

"Yup!" I said, rather comically.
"I need to know you'll be okay after I leave you, and nothing does that better than knowing you got over a douchebag ex."

She casts the other half of her smile.

That was it. A smile was all I wanted for her. In all my own pain and heartbreak, I'd learned that smiles and laughter were the only things that heal. And it didn't matter if they were mine or those of strangers; their mere presence was enough to mend my ailing heart. And I desperately wanted the same for her. I could tell she had woven herself a very comfortable cocoon of depression, but it was time to become a colourful butterfly.

She started to tell me about her ex, reluctantly at first, but the more she spoke, the more her mild dislike for him temporarily clouded the misery we both knew waited for her at the other end of this journey. She told me of how his love was the worst kind of greed, how he took every bit of her and gave nothing back. And in the rare times he did try to give, he was the kind of person who took pleasure in knowing that all the happiness she felt was only a shadow of the love he had shown her, and he could choose to make someone else happy- so he did, many times.

"How about you, tell me about your first heartbreak." She asked me in almost the same breath as her story; obviously intent on not giving me anytime to process all she had just said.

"Well the first girl I ever loved was lightyears beyond me- I had to pretend to be someone better than I was just to get her attention. And when we did date, she came to hate the man I had become for her- and I hated her for it. In the end, we both got the people we thought we wanted to love, only to find those were the kinds of people we could never love."

"You basically said everything without saying anything. I'd like to hear more."

"You're a stranger; I'm not gonna cry all over you the first time we meet," I said with a smile.

She laughed.

I had succeeded.

...

Our train approached its final destination. It was a goodbye I dreaded because I knew I was going to leave the chance of ever seeing her again to the uncertain hands of fate.

As we both reluctantly strolled out of the train station, destined to head in two separate directions, I reached for her hand, shook it and said

"I'm Sean, by the way."

"Nice to meet you, Sean, I'm Sarah."

Paper Planes.

I made my way through the living room into the garden, and saw Wale in the field dressed in clownish clothes, holding two squirt guns, playing with a dozen 5 to 6-year-olds. He was never afraid of looking foolish; his mother always told him "folly is inherent in bravery, so the bravest people sometimes seem like the most foolish people."

"I thought you were coming to see me yesterday" he shouted, in an attempt to make himself heard over the loud children.

"I was, but something urgent came up, and I had to head back to Manchester for the night (I got back on the train to meet Sarah). I got on the 10am train back to London this morning." I answered confidently, knowing I had an open invitation to visit him whenever I wanted.

"Okay, hope everything is fine, though?"

"Well, it's getting better."

"I agree; you sound less distraught now than when you called yesterday. So tell me, what was it that got you so upset that you called almost in tears, what was it you wanted to see me about?"

"Uh, I'm not sure now is the time, Wale," I replied quickly, in an attempt to sway him from this conversation. He was almost twice my age, but he had me call him by his first name every time, and that made me feel like I could really talk to him.

"Go on, Sean." He said, still having his squirt gun standoff against a rather ruthless band of infant mercenaries. He was a one-man army.

"Well it's about my business, I said. I'm yet to find investors, sales are terrible, non-existent even, and I'm behind on so many payments, all the staff have left. I think I have failed, Wale. I think I have failed again. Maybe it's time to count my losses and go back to Nigeria, where it's easier. I think-"

"When did you stop believing in yourself?" he said, interrupting me, unimpressed by my faithless demeanour.

"I don't know that I have, I think I still do. I just don't see the way out. Maybe it's safer to go back and do something else for a while." I said defensively, completing what I had to say before he abruptly cut me off.

It was at this point he forfeited his water-wars with the kids, dropped his gun and led me to sit closer to the adults. He ordered two glasses of lemonade for the both of us. When they came, he drank half of his and lingered in his thoughts for a while. Then, finally, he leaned closer to give voice to those thoughts without too many people hearing what he had to say.

"I had this friend; he started on this entrepreneurship path with me. He was, and still is the most gifted person I know, but I could always tell when his faith was wavering, and I could tell when he lost it altogether.

He usually started by forgetting things; little things like the simple truths he was once sure of. Truths about who he was, why he was here. Then he forgot bigger things like birthdays, anniversaries, meetings. And he kept on forgetting until he no longer remembered the things that really mattered, he no longer remembered what his dreams were, or what he believed in, or why he ever believed in the first place.

We start losing faith when we start forgetting, are you forgetting, Sean?" He asked forcefully, looking square into my eyes. He rarely spoke directly to me. He was the kind that gave advice in zen-like pellets of wisdom and left you to figure your way out yourself. To hear him speak so assertively made me really think about my answer.

"No," I said, with an almost palpable zest of doubt.

"To stop dreaming in the face of trials is how we prepare to fail, Sean. You have to keep your dreams alive when the tests come because dreams are the anchors our future successful selves hold on to. Now is not the time to give up on your dreams and go back to Nigeria, boy.

Nothing is ever easy in the beginning: it wasn't for me either. You know my story, don't you; how I lost everything and had to move back into my wife's parents' house, and live in the same room my wife grew up in with my first son. Those were dark days: that was a storm, but you don't focus on the storms so much that you forget the dreams you believe in.

You see, walking on water is how God expects we ride out storms. He expects you to do the impossible – believe even in the face of doubt." He said assuredly, then took a huge gulp of his lemonade, sighed and continued to talk.

"When Anne and I look back, we always wonder how we even got through those dark days. You just have to believe you can do the impossible because impossible situations are the most common things on your way to success- the path to success is riddled with many impossibilities!"

His mother in law had been listening in. His voice often grew louder the more animated he got. She looked at him, smiled, and nodded: it was obvious she had grown fond of her son-in-law and was proud of how he rose from the ashes. He smiled back at her and continued to talk to me.

"It was a miracle, to be honest; a series of favourable circumstances just converged and made things work out after everything had gone awry for so long. But miracles are never born out of doubtful actions, No! Taking steps of faith is how we make opportunities for miracles. You have to believe in yourself boy, you have to believe in those dreams, and trust those dreams to somehow provide the things you need, when you have given them everything you have.

Everything falls apart in the beginning. Even those of us who now build empires began with mere castles in the sand. The storms rolled in and washed our castles away, but we kept building again and again, until we learned to dig deep into ourselves and build our own foundations of faith- and the next time the storms came, our castles remained.

When everything in your life is a work in progress, it will feel a lot like chaos.

I've learned to expect that when the plans I have given my life to seem to fall apart they will always come together in a well-timed, divinely ordered wreckage; more valuable than what I had even imagined. You just have to trust!

Nothing lasts forever, boy...
Except persistence,
- that should last forever.
Persist!"

He was dressed in half of a clown's costume, but it wasn't difficult to take what he said very seriously. I just sat quietly. I could tell he wanted to scold me a whole lot more for being puny in myself. But I could also tell he felt a sense of empathy, knowing exactly where I was in life, and though he was too far gone in success to admit it, he still remembered a time when he felt as I did. He persisted through them, and he wanted me to do the same.

He let some silence simmer the words he had said to me, while we watched over the children as they played.
He then continued to talk.

"Children are so full of wonder; they see the wonder in everything, don't they?" He asked as we watched them play without any cares. It was his second son's fifth birthday, the kids had made planes for themselves out of wrapping papers and were now going wild with this new handmade toy.

He looked at his 5-year-old and smiled.

"You see Mike tossing his tiny paper plane in the air; he chases it, and every time it lands, he picks it up and throws it again. Maybe if like children playing with paper planes we always picked our dreams back up when they fell, and toss them in the air again and again, maybe then we'd all have something in our adult lives to always marvel about."

He paused for another minute, then he said excitedly, as though inspired by something beyond him "come with me!"

He led me through his house into his personal office. The office was a sharp contrast to the rest of the mansion's old Victorian style architecture. It was a minimalist, grey space with only three notable pieces of furniture; a glass work desk, a huge bookshelf that flushed seamlessly with the wall, and a Natuzzi recliner that doubled as his work seat and a comfort seat.

The most impressive thing was the garden atrium that faced his work desk. It was a horticultural masterpiece that made the rest of the mansion feel like a man-made afterthought built around it. The whole office was set up in a way that proved he wanted to be in constant communion with nature or the force behind it.

He reached for a notepad in his shelf, tore out a sheet, thought for a minute, and scribbled something on it[3]. He folded it, placed it neatly in my jacket pocket, then tapped me three times on my left shoulder and said;

"Read this, when you're most afraid, and when you feel everything is going to shit!"

"Okay," I replied, gratefully. I knew better than to ask what it was he had written. He enjoyed being an enigma, and I felt privileged to be close enough to him that he cared to write me a prescription for my fears. I was lucky to have Wale as a mentor.

"Now let's go back out there and have some fun, I've got another clown costume for you if you want," he said laughing mischievously mid-sentence. "Although I'm not sure it would fit now; you're looking very skinny."

I laughed as well because the call to join him in folly was in his own way a call to bravery. As we made our way back, I felt my phone vibrate. It was a Facebook notification and a couple of messages from Sarah that read:

"I enjoyed chatting with you on the train yesterday. We should meet up again sometime. When are you free? Sorry for the very late response, I've been off social media for a while."

---

[3] Testing of your Faith. Pg. 23

TESTING OF YOUR FAITH.

It's the time in-between
when one expects to see a thing
and when that thing is actually seen
that all hope will seem bested,
and a man's faith truly tested.

From Wale
To Sean

FIRST DATE

All the things we're convinced of today
began as maybes yesterday.
Perhaps that's all Love at first sight is...
Perhaps that's all you are...
Perhaps that's all this date would bring...
A maybe,
I would one day believe.

From Sean
To Sarah

PERFECT FIT

I need to know how it feels to have your fingers trapped in the
gaps between mine; to have your lips grappling tirelessly with
my own. I'm curious to hold your hand, and kiss you, and test
if you were truly made to fill all of my empty spaces... Or if
you're one of those one-size-fits-all kind of lovers - who either
love too much or love too little; but are never really my perfect
fit.

From Sarah
To Sean

A LITTLE BIT OF ETERNITY

"When we love- I mean really, really love, we have a chance to live forever. And it doesn't matter whether it's a person, a job or an idea; our passions are the only things that breed our immortality." Sarah said as she smeared a splash of crimson paint on an empty canvas.

"Do you love art?" she asked the class of twenty-something girls, "then a splash of paint is a little bit of your eternity." She added.

It was our fourth date, and I had arrived early to pick her up from the school she volunteers at, teaching art to young teenagers on Friday evenings. I snuck with clandestine precision into one of her classes just to see what she was like when she didn't know I was watching.

She was just as captivating, talking to a crowd as she was when she laughed, or when she did anything else.

I knew she was the kind of girl who fell in love with something the moment she had decided that it had the slightest potential for beauty; from that moment onwards, she gave all of herself to it. And to her, it didn't matter if it broke her a million times over, she kept giving until others saw the beauty she had seen. In a way, it was the pieces of herself she gave that eventually made those things she loved beautiful. In every way, I wanted to be loved by her. I wanted to be the mosaic of her efforts that people admired.

"Where are we going to this time?" I asked, knowing she was quite the connoisseur, and we were both better off letting her choose restaurants.

"My place," she said, excitedly.

"Your place?"

"Yeah, I'm making our dinner tonight. I live just a few minutes from here," she added.

"Okay, I'm gonna go bring the car around then," I said, already jingling my keys.

"Ooh, we're walking there. I live just a few minutes from here", she said again.

She packed up her things hastily, skilfully dealing with the constant interruptions from her needy students who wanted some of her extra attention. I waited for her by the door, prepping my mind to walk through this cold, snowy night to wherever she lived.

...

As we braved the cold night, making our way to her apartment, we walked towards a mariachi band playing some old Mexican ballad. Their music was contagious; you know the kind of melody that always makes you want to fall in love just to feel what it was like to hold someone you loved while you swayed to it. Sarah caught the bug. She ran into their midst, dropped her bag of paint tools on the pavement, stretched out her arms and shouted from across the distance
 "Come dance with me, Sean!"

I am one of those sane people who gets shy dancing in public, but magical moments like these are reserved only for the brave: and I know you only get a handful of chances to make memories like these all your life. I reached for her hand and joined her in the madness.

We swayed and danced to the sweet melody until our souls were content, and our bodies were warm with love. There is always a chance romance can happen anywhere two lovers are happy enough not to care.

...

"Hmm, smells like chicken," I said, as we walked through the door to her place. She had been slow cooking something in the oven all day, and the aroma had both the air and me alive with delicious expectations.

"Everything smells like chicken to you" she joked as she undid her jacket, and placed it on a coat rack. She then made her way to the oven to check on the Chicken chasseur she had left there.

"But you're right; it is chicken. She added."

...

"I see cooking is one of your many virtues- that was a gastronomic delight," I said, as I greedily finished the serving she had given me.

She smiled, "Yeah, my mum's a chef, but I'm not sure she would be impressed by this."

"Well I am," I added selfishly, knowing she brimmed every time she received a compliment; and I always wanted to see her brim.

We spent the rest of the date keeping ourselves warm with mulled wine and hearty laughter- then it was almost midnight.

"It's time for me to head back." I said, "It's getting late Sarah, and I wouldn't want to-"

"Stay!" She said. Completely cutting me off mid-sentence, and sending me into a brief whirlwind of confused thoughts.
I knew her boundaries; I had learned to share them. If not for anything other than to preserve her conscience- it seemed to be the lifeblood of all her wonder. So her asking me to stay meant she really didn't want to be alone.

"It's my birthday on Sunday, remember?" She said, expecting me to know why that meant "stay."

I knew it was her birthday alright, but it wasn't until now that I realised that meant it was John's birthday too. It was her first birthday without her fraternal half. Now I understood why she didn't want to be alone. I also lived alone, and I knew that the times I felt most lonely and empty were right after a friend just left my place- no one really wants to sleep alone after a great night; it's hardwired into our social DNA's.
Feeling a bit insecure and unsure I had the strength to gird up the lusts in my loins tonight; I asked why she didn't have any of her friends over to spend the weekend with her.

"John and I shared most friends, now every new memory with them always feels incomplete, and every joke seems to be at his expense like we are hiding something from him. I don't want to feel that way, not now. In some ways, you remind me of him. But not in the way that makes me sad. The both of you have this thing you do; you walk around with your heads in the clouds and a rhythm in your step like you can hear a melody other people don't. It's annoying, really." She laughed.

Her laughter is all of my eternity.

"It's those things I want to remember..." She continued, as she loaded the dishwasher with the plates, cleaning up, and avoiding eye contact with me.

"Are you staying?" she asked again, this time with a lot more command in her voice.

"Of course, I am."

That night was the first time I held her as close to me as it was humanly possible for two people to hold each other without fatally crashing into each other's souls.

THE UNWORTHY PILGRIM

Hers was a seductively deep faith that never enforced its
devotion on anyone, but left you to fall hopelessly in love with
the grace with which she went by her things. It was what I
found most attractive about her: the grace.

It was habitual for me to savour minute details of her as if she
was a scenery I expected would soon fade. The skin tight jeans
she'd often wear that sculpted her into a goddess. The way she
matches gold earrings with a rogue silver stud in the lost
piercing on the top of her left ear. The black dress... oh that
black dress, that trickles intimately from her shoulders to her
feet like droplets of rain. She often looked like a living,
breathing paradox of something you'd revere and something
you'd want to ravish.

All day I'd imagine unravelling her completely: just to see what
lied underneath the effortless charm she oozed off. It was my
greatest temptation. She was a beautiful temple filled to the
brim with the Spirit of God: and I was the unworthy pilgrim
longing to come in.

In a way, you become the things you love, don't you? I could
tell that some of her good was rubbing off my bad. Business
meetings yielded profitable results; investors didn't back out at
the last minute; suppliers stopped disappointing. It was as if
with her, my existence was becoming completely new. I never
denied that the image of her glee whenever she heard the good
news was the rabbit's foot I held on to in my mind when I did
business: but I often worried that some of my bad had rubbed
off on her... It didn't, she remained immune to my numerous
vices.

This is how much my days were ruled by thoughts of her. I had
never loved anything so much, not even the things I had lived
and died for countless of times. And that's why it was

impossible for me to imagine why on earth she was convinced that my dreams were more important to me than she'd ever be, and why this was something so real to her that it caused a fight[4].

[4] Quiet Monuments. Pg. 54

All of Paris in the summer

Jonah was one of those special people who really knew how to be a friend. You see, when people have come into your life and drifted away as much as they have in mine you'd find that people like Jonah, who knew how to always be there are very rare. He had a way of always making you know he could see you, no matter how far away you were. Consistent communication was his super power.

Etim was one of those people who listened. He was a diverse soul you could hold a philosophical conversation with one minute, laugh about something completely unrelated the next, then delve right into matters of the heart after that. With him, there were never deep or shallow conversations; it was always just wholesome banter that somehow made you question things and left you wiser. He knew a lot about a lot of things: I'm not sure whether it's because he listened, or whether it was because he read too much.

Gabriel was the kind of guy that helped- the kind to make sacrifices at his own expense. He was good at a lot of things that made lots of money and made life fun for us while we were in Uni. He wrote code, built websites, Dj'd, and was one now of Nigeria's most recognised graphic designers. Of the four of us, he was the one girls most flocked around. I think it was his smile and his homely voice that drew them to him; his voice always radiates the same type of warmth that makes women take their clothes off in summer. The pretty girls the rest of us were too shy to talk to all seemed to want to talk to him, and he always knew how to share the attention.

We had all been flatmates, back in our undergrad days. We had shared deadlines, cutlery, chores, and a gentle revolt against parental control. It had been four years since we all were together, and we were all meeting because Jonah, who had picked up golfing as a hobby right after leaving school was now putting holes in the big leagues. None of us were married yet, and although we had all experienced many good fortunes in our lives after school, this was the first big thing we had to celebrate.

"It's good to visit Paris when you're single," Etim said, as he breathed in the lovely sight from the flat we had rented to share for the weekend. He was the only one presently not in a serious relationship. He recently chose to be single for a while, but the rest of us knew all too well, that he had a lot more love in him than the three of us could muster.

"All the girls, yeah?" Gabriel replied, tapping Etim on his shoulder with a wide grin on his face.

"No, it's not just that, it's the architecture of the town. It's designed to be personal. All the skyscrapers are on the outskirts, and the city is kept as it was, both aged and modern. It's what makes Paris so intimate that you can't help but fall passionately in love with it though it is completely inanimate and incapable of loving you back. Isn't that what true love is — giving and expecting nothing back? In a way, being in Paris teaches us how to fall in love."

"Guys, Etim has started with his deep quotes this weekend," Gabriel shouted from the terrace into the high-ceilinged living room. His voice filled the whole room with the makings of familiar humour.

Jonah and I looked at each other and chuckled; we knew Etim was in a rather reflective mood; we were very careful not to laugh at his expense. He had just had his heart broken by someone he moved the earth for, but Gabriel hadn't been filled in on the gist yet. So, we called him and filled him in.

"Let's go for a walk Guys," Jonah said, in an attempt to jolt us into our usual youthful frenzy. Apart from celebrating his success, he also planned on getting a ring to propose to his girlfriend, and he wanted us to be a part of it. He was the kind of person that made you a part of the important moments in his life.

"Let's do this!" he exclaimed. That was a thing we usually said to psyche ourselves into excitement. It didn't even seem strange our relatively young ages that taking a walk was what we considered exciting. It wasn't uncommon for us to begin days by taking walks, and end them in a rave. As long as four of us were together, everything we did had the chance at starting a party.

...

As we all walked down the street that led from the Arc de Triumph to the Louvre, we took in all of Paris in the summer, unadulterated by the filters of sunglasses. It wasn't long until we noticed something was missing from everyone we walked past, it was worry, and concern. Everyone seemed happy like they had never had a worry in their entire lives. Black or white, it didn't matter; they were all just happy- too happy for us not to debate about.

"People can't be this happy!" Etim exclaimed.

"The French are happy people," Gabriel replied.

"It's Paris, it's not just filled with the French, it's filled with tourists too," I said.

"Yeah, but the French are still one of the happiest people in the world, aren't they?" Jonah added.

"That's a myth" Etim replied.

It felt appropriate to argue if the French would be different in the small towns- those towns that are so nucleated and honest that it was impossible to have the truth diffused and hidden from the sight of tourists.

You know those small towns where people work with their hands and the waitress at the town bar knows almost everyone's name, address and pain medication. Those towns where happiness and misery are such shared commodities that to pretend to have either when you didn't would be a grievous sin - that's where you test the myth about a people.

We argued logically, and we argued irrationally. It was our thing.

We continued to walk all about Paris, unconcerned about getting lost. Gabriel and Jonah got thirsty and stopped to get a drink at an unassuming kiosk. Etim and I continue to walk further down, expecting they'd catch up to us in their own time. I had hoped to get a minute to really know what led to his break up with the girl he once described as "the only revelation that didn't reveal herself in a ball of light but in empirical and proven acts of trust." He was different in the way he saw things. That's what made him a savant.

"So, bro" I started to say carelessly.
"What happen-?"
Two deafening cracking sounds from the building closest to us burst their way into the middle of my sentence. Along with them came a wall of heat that numbed all my senses and pushed me across the pavement. It was a bomb.

...

I woke up to the faint sound of distant wailing, ringing ears, a bleeding nose, and no signs of any broken bones.

Jonah and Gabriel ran to help me up. I could tell they were worried and shouting for my attention , but all I heard was a buzzing noise... Suddenly my senses return; the sound of their confused screams piercing through my ears - what I hear fills me with dread.

"Where is Etim?
Where is Etim!"

I looked around to see only his left shoe, amidst the garbage of broken concrete and human parts that littered the smoke-filled street.

36 people died that day.

HARBINGERS OF HOPE

"What's your favourite childhood memory?" Sarah asked, as she curled into a ball and laid her head down on my thigh.

"That's hard to remember," I said. "My childhood seems to be a blur of infant crime, parental punishment and hours of self-exile into solitude, building cities out of old cassette tapes in our family living room. I enjoyed imagining building things; I did it all day, sometimes."

"Okay, Mr. Loner who builds cities out of old cassette tapes. What childhood experience do you think affected your adult life the most?"

"Let me think about that," I replied.
"Okay, you notice this slight limp I have?"

"Yes," she said quickly.

"Well when I was about 13, I got hit by a motorcycle in Lagos, it's why I have this terrible scar on my head as well."

"Oh, I never noticed that." She said jokingly.
"Is that it? You know I know this already."

"No, it's not. After the crash, and the usual commotion that ensues when there is an accident in Lagos, I was rushed to the nearest hospital. I remember the theatre walls were a depressing shade of brown, and the asbestos ceiling - which was the most I saw of the hospital - seemed to be damp in every place it was possible to be damp without falling apart.

I was brought into the hospital unconscious and bleeding. I woke up on the theatre table to a doctor and three nurses working to save me. I remember trying to move my leg, and my broken femur piercing my thigh. It was the most excruciating pain I've ever felt; I was in hell in my own body."

She sighs, as she patted my left thigh like a wounded puppy. I continued to talk, as I ran my fingers through her hair.

"I pulled one of the theatre nurses close to me as soon as I could, still unsure what exactly had happened to me the last few minutes...

"You were in an Okada (motorcycle) accident," she said, "you've broken your leg."

"Accident? I broke my leg?" I replied, completely confused...

"How bad is it?" I asked.

"Very bad!" She answered distracted, and a little unconcerned.

"Will I ever walk again," I asked her immediately,

"No," She replied, with no consideration for my fragile state of existence- Incompetence is sometimes revealed in bad manners.

I've never believed a single word could be powerful enough to convey such doom that the person who hears it wishes for death, and is immediately granted his wish... I passed out, out of sheer hopelessness. They all resumed their efforts to revive me.

By then, my dad had been told of my present state. You know he's a medical doctor, right? He was on his way to me already, driving his ambulance himself madly like the '*firewos*' that smuggle cars across country borders into Lagos. He drove so recklessly that a day after my accident his closest friend called him and told him to fire the driver that drove that Wednesday because he was a mad man.

I don't remember much about my Dad picking me from that brown walled hospital; I was too busy fiddling with the Shakespearean question 'to be or not to be.' I do remember being brought into his hospital, and being placed in the X-ray room. I could tell exactly where I was then; these were the places my childhood memories were made of.

They placed me gently on the X-ray table, having stopped all of my bleeding orifices in the ambulance. My mother walks into the room. Dad hadn't told her anything before he left to rescue me - he is my hero. This was the first time she was seeing her son bandaged on the head, half crippled and blistered all over his frail body with 16 other stitch worthy lacerations.

I saw her; it was the only time I ever saw her cry. It was at this point in my life that I knew that love was something that could be felt; I mean really felt in all of your being. I could feel her love for me literally pour out of her faster than the tears rolled down her face.

"Mum, am I going to walk again?" I asked.

"Yes," she said immediately.
"Yes, you will, you will... Your dad and I will make sure you do!" She said convincingly, while still trying to grasp this new reality that life had violently tossed at her.

I stopped talking to Sarah altogether now, thinking to myself how much those words still meant to me... Then I continued.

"I think parents are meant to be eternal harbingers of hope; I think their actions and their words are supposed to be lifelong sources of hope for their offspring. My mother is a nurse you see, just like the woman at the first hospital; and don't get me wrong, the other nurse was right about my chances of ever walking again. They were almost none existent. My femur had broken too close to my knee to be fixed by standard methods, and my nerves were practically dead - and if you know anything about nerve damage, there is no telling whether or not they'd ever work again.

After days of being advised that complete amputation was the only viable option, I watched my parents muster 9 months of constant medical and financial miracles to get me stand upright again. I remember clearly on those days when I saw no progress, and my foot and toes still didn't respond to my own thoughts; my mother's promise to me was my only source of hope - and my reason to keep trying. In a way, it still is, at my most vulnerable times. It's how I learned to believe that impossible things happen when you wholeheartedly hold on to a heartfelt promise from someone who really loves you; in a way she taught me how to believe in God.

Love makes promises and does everything to make those promises come true. That's where miracles come from.

Love always hopes for the best, I think. When someone really loves you, they will always want the best for you; they never settle for anything less. They'd work for it, pray for it, sacrifice everything for it, and make it come true by being sources of unconditional support and faith in your trying times. They will fight the odds for you, even if you think you don't deserve it.

It's why for me, Love only feels real, when all the emotions that brought us together actually drive us to always do good to each other, to always hope for the best for each other, and to always go out of your way to make sure that the best you desire for them really does come true. That's how you know that your love is a real kind of love; it's sustained by a selfless eternal hope."

HUMAN CONNECTIONS

We are all humans connecting
like the machines we create.

Our wandering eyes align.
We connect, it's wireless.
No words spoken yet,
but you can tell I'm made to rip you to shreds
and I can tell you're made to let me.

We hold hands
like two gears in motion,
each one depends on the other
to stay alive...
each one depends on the other
to keep moving.

Our lips touch,
our bodies kiss.
Surface contact,
full body contact.
It's inevitable-
all that your flesh has to give:
in heat,
in moans,
in quiver
and in cringe,
all,
mine is willing
to receive.

Then I become the pivot upon which
you make you make your twists and turns
- the lever

that thrusts you
body and soul
to ecstatic heights...
So high we both understand
the irrefutability in the welding
together of two naked sheets,
and the permanence in
the mechanics of the screwing
of bolts to nuts
in a perfect well-oiled union.

In the end, we realise
that we are merely humans
making connections
like the machines
we create.

THE PARTS OF US THAT MAKE MAGIC HAPPEN.

"When are you going to talk to her?" Sarah asked for the third time, intent on convincing me that reaching out to my ex was a good idea.

I knew Sarah was self-destructive in a weird way. Her self-destruction stemmed from her belief that we only stand the chance of gaining the most happiness from the actions that could also bring us the most pain. She always risked self-destruction at a chance of a fuller, more absolute happiness. I had watched her do it many times, and now she was about to do it with us.

She was the kind to risk one lifetime for an eternity - the kind to make one heap of all the earth she had worked for and toss it at the slightest chance at a piece of heaven. I wasn't, and I wasn't having any of her suggestions to call up my ex and meet with her since she was in town for her friend's graduation.

"Sean. I can tell there is still a part of you that she owns," she said, worriedly "- the part that asks 'what if?' She still has the part of you that holds on to possibilities and fantasies, and the magic needed to fix broken things. You've filled what's missing with anger and disdain for her...
I want that part of you that she has - because it's the only part that would always imagine and yearn for life with me. It's how I'd know that no matter how far apart we drift, there would always be a chance at finding each other again. I need you to go get the part of you that makes magic happen."

Sarah was right. Thinking about Yemi often began with imagining how life could have been perfect with her, and always degenerated into anger and uncertainty about how we ended, and sometimes an overwhelming desire to reach out to her. It wasn't the same with the other girls I dated. Maybe because I did the breaking, or maybe because Yemi still held on to the part of me capable of regretting a lost love - the only part that could stir up the will to fight and get it back.

"Call her, Sean. Meet with her for coffee or lunch or whatever and get some closure." There was a slight insecurity in her voice. I could tell she was a little uncomfortable with her own suggestions, but the fact she still made them anyways convinced me she had faith in me; in us.

Today's generation of lovers tend to be too insecure and selfish to care if the people they are in love with are whole; they hold on desperately to half of a man or half of a woman- and never care about making them whole. All they care about is getting someone to have and to hold. They are not bothered by how broken the people they claim to love are; they all just desperate to have and hold someone, anyone. Sarah wasn't like that; she wanted me whole. I found it strange.

....

I looked through the window at Manchester's pubescent but promising skyline. I'm sat at Hotel Gotham's Honey, my favourite of the restaurants Sarah introduced me to. I'm never sure why I keep coming back here. Perhaps it's the restaurant's intimate ambience reminiscent in its name, or maybe it is the buzz that courses through you with every mouthful. Whatever it is, I always find myself coming back for more. I was sure why I picked it this time though; I had a point to prove.

Yemi had agreed to meet for a late lunch. It was surprisingly easy to convince her. I had always thought that the next time we saw it would either be by chance, or by some desperate attempt to manipulate fate. But it wasn't. I was so nervous that the waiter, Ryan, offered me a drink on the house. Maybe Sarah was right; Yemi still had a part of me. Maybe that's what happens when someone breaks your heart; they hold on to pieces it, and the nervousness you feel whenever you're around them is simply your heart calling out to its missing parts.

Yemi walks into the room; petite and bright. The whole restaurant has a moment with her. She was always a showstopper, and I was always a sucker for those things around which time stood still.
She wasn't any more beautiful than an average day, yet I was always drawn to her like a bird to heights. That's the mystery of ordinary people; they appear mundane, but that doesn't stop them from drawing us in and trapping our souls within their supernatural.

"Hey," she said as she pulled her chair to sit.

"Hey," I responded, coldly. I had resolved in my mind to be as transactional and aloof as I could. But no one fixes broken bridges with a lackadaisical attitude, and you sure as hell don't mend broken hearts with it.

"Kilon shei eh? (What the hell is wrong with you?)" She asked in our native Yoruba dialect with a smile on her face, and with a let's pick up right where we left off tone in her voice.

I laughed. She knew I'd find her question funny because we both often laughed at how horrible she was at speaking Yoruba. She always had a way of breaking my most fortified walls with the shortest phrases.

"How are you?" She asked immediately, seizing the opportunity in my careless laughter.

"I'm good."

"I know you are... I saw your interview on BellaNaija. You're doing great, and I'm very proud of you."

"Thanks" I replied, proudly. I felt I had the upper hand: I clenched on to it with a confident smile, and I wasn't going to let it go.
"And you, how have you been?" I asked, secretly hoping she'd tell me she was miserable, and you know, burst out into a tearful tale of how she was stupid for letting me go... I knew she was fine: she had started a very profitable blog. I knew she was engaged to a great guy; I knew she was happy: I knew all these things but still hoped anyways - like we all do when we meet with an ex that broke us in two.

"I've been superb," she said as she flaunted her engagement ring at me.

"I see you're happy," I said, with some disappointment still lingering in my voice.

"I am," she interjects passionately. Her passion was always infectious.

"That's nice to hear. I -"

"Would you like to place your order now, sir," Ryan interrupts, saving me from what was almost certainly going to be an awkward moment. He's got my back; I better leave him the biggest tip of his life.

"Yes, we would," I answered.

I had no intention of bringing up our past at the restaurant. I merely wanted to show her a bit of the life I lived now. She wasn't thrown by any of it: I'm not sure why I thought she would. My new reality was her every day.

Great meals make for the best small talk.

The rest of the evening we savoured every bit of our Chef's impeccable dishes, laughed about politics and had a feisty debate about Game of Thrones during desert. In that moment, and in that restaurant, we forgot about the things that tore us apart and lingered only in the things that brought us together.

...

"Let me show you a bit of Manchester," I said, as we walked out of the lift and made our way out of the hotel.
"Okay," she answered, excitedly. She was always one for adventures.

"You always told me that the best way to discover a new city is by walking... So, we're gonna walk around town, and when we get tired, I'll get you a taxi. Okay?"

"Okay. Sounds like a plan."

It wasn't until long that we wandered around the city and into the conversation we both avoided all evening. After fifteen minutes of making pseudo-diagnosis about why we couldn't work, I got fed up and just asked;

"What actually happened with us, Yemi? Tell me, because I honestly don't know, and I think not knowing makes it worse for me."

You need to understand; I was clueless throughout our so-called break up it felt more like a breakdown. We never even had any discussion to end it. I remember us having one all too familiar argument about my poor communication after which she slowly disappeared from my existence; fading like the memory of a rainbow in the sky.

"We argued a lot," she replied.

"Yes, we did, but that's not what ended us, Yemi. We argued, but I remember we always respected each other's opinions. For me it was the cold conversations, it was you making me talk to silence at the other end of the line for months. It was trying so hard to make you laugh and failing, not because the jokes weren't funny to you, but because you had made up your mind not to find any joy in me anymore. It was cold, Yemi, and I was angry at you for it... It broke me in ways I never thought I could be broken, I think it still breaks me. It wasn't until I tried to love again, I realised that I had become an insecure jerk who hurts people, who forces them to walk on the broken pieces of me you left behind, and who remained unapologetic about hurting them."

"It's funny that's how you see it, Sean," she replied, "because from my point of view it was you who was silent. You never talked to me about anything. You carried your dreams and your fears on your head, they were yours, and I wasn't allowed to share.

But you knew everything about me, everything!

You never really talked to me. And my silent treatment, that was me giving you a taste of your own medicine. And maybe I took it too far or let it drag on for too long. But you always left me to hear important things about you from other people. I remember hearing you got fired from your job from someone else several weeks after it had happened. And all that while you were talking to me, making me believe everything was all right with you. That was it for me. You never shared your problems with me, only your victories..."

"Maybe I thought you deserved the spoils of war, not the scars of the battle," I said, defensively.

"There you go again using words to make things more beautiful than they really are." She said with a smile.

"But you know I could have changed... Remember how I was when we met, our first year at Uni? "

"Ah, I remember, you were something else: a rebel with no cause."

"Yes, I was, but I changed. I became better; I became better because of you. It's why it felt so terrible to be slowly abandoned by you without any form of a goodbye" I said, fearlessly revealing my broken parts.

She sighed, then took a deep breath,
"I'm sorry you felt that way. But the more I look back, the more I think that maybe I was only supposed to love you into becoming the person who cared desperately about his dreams, and let someone else love you into an even better man. I had no doubt you could change, but I wasn't sure I had it in me to do the work. It's not that I didn't love you; it's that somewhere in trying to make you better, I felt I was missing out on building myself as well.

And you, you were becoming the kind of person I imagined you could be, not who you really were on the inside. It's obvious to me now that the parts of you that were missing were parts my love couldn't fill at that point in our lives. You know we both wanted to go out and wholeheartedly reach for our dreams, but we both didn't know how to do that and still remain at each other's side. That's not something we could learn as a young couple without resenting each other when our dreams failed.

The truth is you had done such a good job becoming the better man I thought you could be, that the only way you could ever become anything more was if I let you go. I see that clearly now."

She stops for a breath or two and then continues.

"I'm sorry I didn't handle things well, I really didn't know how to let you go, and I honestly didn't want to - but deep down I think I knew that you weren't mine to love forever. I really didn't know how to say all these then without sounding heartless and bitter- it's why I just didn't say anything."

I had imagined a million and three ways this conversation would go. This definitely wasn't one million and four. I wasn't the slightest bit angry with her anymore. Somewhere in the middle of our conversation, I had a newfound respect and love for her. I know now being older and slightly wiser how important it is to share your fears with those close to you; to let them carry your burdens with you. I've learned how important it is to allow friends lead you through the dark, and to let lovers feel like they are part of your struggle. It's the only way trust is built, and bonds forged stronger. It's the quickest way to make people feel indispensable to your very existence.

In my life after Yemi, I had learned that in love, sometimes it's the thrill of winning together that give a lover a reason to fight for your dreams; and it's that desire to keep fighting your dreams that inadvertently keeps you together!

I never gave Yemi the opportunity to help me through my dark times. For me then, it was a sign of weakness. Yet I expected her to stay long enough to enjoy the good times. Foolish... Childish!

"I'm so sorry, Yemi," I said, relieved of a lot of the anger and resentment I had bottled up towards her.

"I'm sorry too Sean. I'm sorry I didn't have the courage to say the things I was feeling then, and that I left you in the dark for so long, without closure."

Somehow I felt a little bit whole; I think she did too.

We continued to talk late into the night, handing apologies back and forth; exchanging the pieces of each other we both selfishly held on to all these years.

WHY WE FORGIVE

It's hard to believe
That the ones who broke our hearts
Hold the pieces
To put them back together again

...

It's why we forgive-
It's the only way to find
The missing pieces
That could make us whole again

From Sarah
To Sean

QUIET MONUMENTS

"No one understands love better than the One who taught colours to mix: who showed blue what parts of red made purple, and what parts of me made you" That's what Sarah said to me the day she made both her faith and her boundaries clear.

She'd always wanted to get married in an old church; you know those 15th-century cathedrals that were made of finely carved grit, wood and gold carvings, candlelit chandeliers, and stained glass windows. To her they were proof that beauty could be kept pristine; that earthly things became divine if we only loved them enough to preserve them. She always believed our love story would be something of a cathedral - a quiet monument to a time when love was God.

"To love and be loved right back is such a rare and powerful and precious coincidence." The preacher said. "It's why marriages are divine - it's two people choosing to make a mere coincidence last a lifetime." As he spoke, I couldn't help the feeling that maybe he sounded rather familiar.

The preacher continued to rouse the crowd skillfully as he made his way to the "I do's," I nervously fiddled with the sleeve buttons on my ivory tux, thinking to myself "she's definitely gonna say I do, isn't she?" I calmed my nerves by reminding myself of something she had written to me six months into our cathedral love affair. You see, of the two of us, I never considered myself the poet, because she, she was something more. Her letters to me were filled with the many things she was too afraid to say and the most beautiful words I had ever read.

The note that stayed my nerves she wrote at a time when we had both let our insecurities get the best of us. It was a time when I felt unsure I'd be able to provide for the life she deserved, she was uncertain I had any love left to share outside my dreams. Two insecurities never make a quiet argument. It was the first and only time we broke up.[5]

We'd agreed early on in our relationship that if we ever had a big fight, we would meet a few days later with clear heads at our favourite coffee shop. We decided we would hand each other a note- no longer than 10 lines, telling the other how we really felt. We often wrote to each other, but when we fought, we had the 10 line rule because it forces you to think of what is most important. We sat together without saying a word. We just held hands; she had a hot chocolate, and I sipped coffee. Then she gave me her note[6], scribbled on the back of our rumpled Starbucks receipt, and I handed her mine[7].

I read hers, three times over, and knew immediately that she was my forever.

---

[5] The Unworthy Pilgrim. Pg. 31
[6] Flesh & Blood; Ink & Word. Pg. 56
[7] Lost and Found Pg. 57

FLESH & BLOOD; INK & WORD

If God so loved the world
that He gave the world His Son[8].
And if God's all great son,
is His word in fleshly form[9].

Then God so loved the world,
he gave the world His word...

So I'm writing this note to you
as proof of my love.
That before flesh, and blood, and son,
came this vow in ink and word.

.

                                    From Sarah
                                    To Sean

[8] John 3:16; The Bible.
[9] John 1:14; The Bible.

LOST AND FOUND

If my heart was ever in a clutter
of items lost and found.
I'm certain that without quarrel or chatter,
it will be mailed directly to your home.

Because written on it
rather boldly is,
your name,
and your address inscribed beneath.

From Sean
To Sarah

I START, YOU FINISH

We are one,
we've always been:
In word,
we complete each other's lines...
I phrase,
you sentence.

Tonight,
we become one
in deed:
Our bodies fuse like poetry...
I verse and squirt,
you syntax and cum.

...

From Sarah
To Sean

AN EXPEDITION OF HER TWIN PEAKS

Dear perky twin peak mountains,
imposing in my horizon,
I have longed to feel you
tremble
underneath me;
And to kiss
the clouds
that rest above you.

So I'll climb
with bare hands
to your climax,
and leave my mark!

That anyone who sees you
without clothes of grass or snow
would want to know

If it be Man,
or Beast,
that did this to you.

From Sean
To Sarah

How my Persistence feels

I reminisce.

The talks into the night, the long walks, the candle lit dinners,
the late night dancing, the spontaneous drop-ins, the awkward
goodbyes, the break ups, the make ups, the many clichés that
led us to this moment where we are finally alone with our lusts.

You Undress…

One piece of guilt at a time, till your black stockings slither
from your naked feet to the wooden floor. It's midnight. You
get more beautiful the less you wear; even innocence unearths
lust, once it's bare.

I've earned this!

Months of never giving in to our desires, and now our duet of
unintelligible words fill the air with Pentecostal vigour. You
beg for God. You beg for more. This is just the beginning; I
will wear your body out as I have your will. Persistence pays
off. I know that now, and now you know that too; you know
now just how my persistence feels like inside you.

You're mine now.

Colour my World, Baby.

Sarah was always someone people flocked around. She was the sunrise that bathed the clouds closest to her with the golden promise of a beautiful day. She was like that; She'd made lifelong friends of people she met on trains or in restaurants or o the street. In an instant, they would be sharing dreams, goals and phone numbers. I was never like that, it took time for me to open up to people, but every time I was around her, I shared some of her magnetism. Isn't that why two people fall in love, to gradually become one?

"It doesn't matter how hard you try, no two people will ever love you the same, and some people will never love you back. Even our hearts are abstract paintings people read different meanings to, and some find no meaning in at all," Sarah said to the new friend she had made on our lift down from the hotel we stayed for our honeymoon.

She always understood the world through art, the canvas, and a paint dipped brush. They opened her mind to a world other people never saw or maybe they were the tools with which she painted the world as she saw it. I never really understood why she never sold any of her paintings. Maybe that's what you do with the things that open up the world to you; you keep them sacred, unadulterated by commerce.

"Hey baby," she called for me as I walked past her. I had left her in the hotel lounge for a few minutes with her new friend and stepped back to the room. I had a quick business emergency to attend to. I winked at her, to let her know I was ready to go chill by the poolside as we had planned. She took a minute to round up with her new friend and caught up with me.

"Didn't you just meet that woman on our lift down earlier?" I asked.

"Yeah?"

"And you're already having an intense heart to heart conversation with her about love and stuff. I never know how you do that - make strangers into friends in less than a minute. It still amazes me."

She laughed off my comment. Usually, she would fill me in about what she was talking about, but this time, she didn't. I could tell she had something on her mind. Whenever she did, her laughter would be shallow as if a nagging thought was stopping joy from digging deeper into her soul.

"I have a gift for you," she finally said after a minute of silence.

"Ooh, okay," I replied confused and a bit disappointed to admit I had not gotten her anything. I never grew up getting gifts from my folks. Don't get me wrong; they always celebrated birthdays and graduations with a party. But their idea of a gift was always cash. They'd give you more cash the older you got, or the better your grades got in school. It's how they taught us never to fear the lack of money, but to always understand that money came with hard work, and sometimes with age. Perhaps that's why it didn't occur to get a typical wedding gift for Sarah.

My idea of a gift had to be something that proved the certainty of our financial future — after all; that was what I was most uncertain about when we dated. I had fully paid for a flat in Manchester and was waiting to surprise her when we got back. We'd never have to worry about where we would sleep, no matter how business went; we'd always have a home. You see, It's the simple things that keep us alive; money in the bank, food in the belly, and the occasional whiff of a lover's scent. I had all those things now, and I never felt more alive.

"Don't worry, I'm not expecting anything from you," she said, now with her deep soul binding, mischievous laugh.

I breathed an inaudible sigh of relief.
"So, what's this gift? You're making me excited."

"It's nothing major, but I think it's the most important thing we can both share." She reached for her summer bag and brought out two black leatherback journals. She handed me mine; my name is inscribed in gold on the front of it and the words "Colour my world with beautiful words," at the back. She held on to hers, and held my hand.

"An empty journal?" I asked, flipping through it, somewhat disappointed.

"Yes a journal, I've made us enough to last a long time. When you fill this, they'd always be more to write in."

"Okay, you want me to start journaling?"

She laughs.
"Hmm, Yes, and No. I don't want you to do anything different from what you're already doing.
Listen, I don't want us to be one of those couples who fight and argue until we have no more good things to say to each other. When that happens, it's never a good sign. When we have no more words to say, thats then we realise how much of love has been lost between us because we both chose not to listen each other.
And I know that sometimes it's hard to say those things on our minds - it's hard for both of us. I'm not expecting that to change in an instant just because we got married. Sometimes, no matter how well two people know each other, their lips still cannot express what their hearts feel. But we can always write, can't we?

"Yeah, I guess so."

"The things we wrote to each other have always been what held us together through everything. Remember that one that time we fought; the words we wrote guided us to back each other. We always wrote them on pieces of paper back then, but the thing about that is, once one piece is missing, so is a part of our story.

Love stories are too important to have a single moment we can't remember or relive.

I want you to write to me as often as you can in this journal. I am going to write to you as often as I can in mine too. At any point in time, we can read what each other wrote. It's how I'd always know for sure that you're still thinking of me, and it's the same for you too. You can pick mine up to read anytime you feel like it, I'd expect the same from you. It's a journal of our love for each other."

I listened to her and nodded. Honestly, I didn't think it would be a problem, I think she knew that. Whenever I put pen to paper, I always became a better man; and because of her, I had learned that the more I wrote about the people I loved, the better I got at loving them. I already wrote about Sarah as often as I could; she was already the muse that made me reach for the moon and the anchor that kept me grounded. She was the myth that inspired me to adventures and the North Star that always led me back home. It's the way lovers are supposed to be. They are not made to be everything; they are only made to be the things that matter most to our lives.

"Sarah, that's a beautiful idea, I like it."

"I know right? I'm amazing like that," she said with a smile.

EMPTY VESSELS

We all think that when love comes, it does one of two things, it either breaks us completely, or it makes us whole. But then there is the kind of love that makes us whole, and leaves us empty? For me, that's the worst fate for two lovers.

I have never feared being broken. I always knew that if I was strong enough to forgive, I could be whole again. What I fear is being empty; having felt a great love and then left empty by the very same person who made me whole. It's a terrible thing living with the person you love, but living without the affection that filled up what their love had made whole.

I fear becoming the empty vessel of an *affectionless* marriage. It's a sickening feeling, having the person you love touch you, and not have it penetrate your soul; seeing them forget the many sentiments that keep your desires burning; hearing them laugh and knowing that the melody your heart once skipped to, is gone.

What do you do then, when there is nothing to forgive, nothing to fight about, yet nothing to hold on to? How do you survive being held together by a commitment to each other, yet driven apart by the nothingness you feel for each other?

You secretly hope they'd do something to break your heart, or make you angry, just so some of that creative chaos can slip back into your dull affair. At least when that happens, you have something to scream, cry and be jealous about - then you have something to feel. It's a dangerous place to be in; desiring pain just to feel something.

It's why this is my first entry into my journal - a reminder of the little things that keep my heart beating for you. The little things you do that set me over the edge, hanging on to you.

I love it when you kiss me on the forehead, and when you wink
at me in the middle of a crowd. I love it when you look at me
like you really see me - like you can read my desire for you on
my face. I love it when you hold me like you have the right to
every inch of my body, pin me to the wall and invade my
privacy. I love it when you sneak tiny notes into my purse and
leave me to find out days after how beautiful you thought I
looked in some dress I no longer remember wearing. I love how
you name every tiny birthmark on my body after pantheon
goddesses. I love it when you ruffle your fingers through my
hair tell me it smells like coconuts, jasmine, and everything you
want in your future. I love how you see the little things about
me that no one else cares to look for and how you surprise me
in ways I could never imagine... I love the way you say my name
like it's a sacred thing and how you remember our moments like
they are the precious stones that make up treasure troves. I love
how you look for me in the sun, moon and stars. I love how
you are never selfish with compliments, and how your anger
knows no foul words.

I love you baby, and I really love how you love me.

From Sarah
To Sean

I WILL BE.

I will be the curve to your smile;
the shine to your eyes.

I will be the good to your bad:
the love to your lust.

I will be the eight of your figure;
the perfect to your picture.

I will be the band on your finger;
the missing to your piece.

I will be the nature to your nurture:
the wild to your tame.

I will be the undoing of your dress;
and the veil to your body.

I will be the arching of your back;
and pleasure within your thighs.

I will be the breaking of your gates;
the soothing of your pain

I will be the fuel for your moans,
and the loud of your noise.

I will be the stalk to your rose;
the prick in your flesh.

I will be the current to your waters;
the rise to your springs.

I will be the guide to your descent,
and the soft of your fall.

I will be the rest for your head,
and the sweet of your dreams.

From Sean
To Sarah

NUCLEAR FUSION

The first time we kissed,
there were no fireworks,
and there were no sparkles.
I didn't want there to be.
Fireworks burn too quick
and sparkles die too fast.

But your kiss always felt a lot like gravity,
inescapable, all-consuming,
and the reason for all life on earth.

Like in the birth of stars,
your gravity slowly pulled together the lost pieces of me;
and ignited me by surprise!

...

Now I burn forever for you
like the brightest sun
in a billion star-studded galaxies.

From Sarah
To Sean

THE LOST VERSE

I was a lost verse
seeking the rhyme to whom I belonged,
-*losting* for rhythm, for structure, for form.

I was a lost verse
trailing the page for one to converse,
lost between lines with no words to love.

I was a lost verse
seeking the rhyme to whom I belonged,
then I met you, and became a song.

From Sarah
To Sean

I saw how much of the old me
was consumed by your fire...

... and hoped to God
You still had a lot more love to burn.

From Sean
To Sarah

ICE PRINCESS

I would slowly unwrap you,
make you thaw...
until there is nothing left.
And as you lose yourself
drifting quietly into the clouds,
I would bring you back to earth
screaming,
in showers of thunderous rain.

Then catch you,

wrap you up,

And begin again.

From Sean
To Sarah

THE CHAOS WE ARE.

"We all hate the *'goodbyes'* we say that never get a *'see you soon.'* Or the *'I'm sorry'* that never gets an *'I forgive you'.* And the *'I love you'* that never gets an *'I love you too.'*

Maybe that's why we dread losing a loved one. Death is the worst kind of goodbye, because it makes you wave and wait your whole life, and never get a wave back. It makes you whisper I'm sorry to the wind, hoping somehow that those you've hurt could hear you, and maybe forgive you. It makes you confess love in the middle of the night to an emptiness on your bedside and get nothing back.

Sometimes these silent responses immortalise the people we've lost making them perfect in our minds like those lovers that never wrote us back, but we still worship. But more often than not it threatens to tarnish the image of them we hold on to dearly in our hearts. Nothing causes heartbreak like a lack of reciprocity.

To our hearts, it doesn't matter if those we love didn't reciprocate because they really couldn't; our hearts don't understand death the way our brains do. Our hearts don't get how anyone could be too far gone to reciprocate a gesture of affection. It's the irrational organ that clouds its madness in steady, trusted monochromatic beats.

To our hearts, reciprocity must always be possible whenever love is felt- no matter the distance. It's why it always sees the lack of it as a void that must be filled. Our hearts numb us from the pain of the unrequited love of our dead in the same way it would when a lover walks out of our lives; by trying to replace every beautiful memory shared with them with something less hurtful and less real.

Usually, when that happens, we also lose the affection we felt for them as well, we slowly begin to resent them for leaving us.

I remember fighting my heart from trying to replace John's loss with something else; I didn't want to resent him for leaving me alone in this world. I remember not allowing meagre things distract me from the pain. I remember mourning long after others had tossed their sorrows with the sand on his casket. I remember envying those who I ever heard say that when you lose someone you love, everything reminds you of them.

I envied them because, after their loss, they pretended that the memory of a thing was sufficient enough to replace the presence of that thing. It isn't!

I never really had that 'everything reminds me of John' phase. I walked into our apartment, and nothing really reminded of him; not his favourite jacket, or the plethora of unfinished to-do lists he'd stuck on our fridge, not the stash of gummy bears he labelled 'everything that's bad for our teeth', or the tattoo of his name I'd intentionally misspelt 'Johan' on my right wrist. They were all mere carcasses of his essence- incapable of bringing anything more than a faint memory of him. They were the useless things his soul had loved and was careless enough to leave behind- and I knew I was one of them.

Somehow in my mourning, I became one of those lifeless things that reminded others of him... It's why I would like to ask those to whom I acted lifeless towards to please forgive me. It was a trying time for me, and sometimes I regret my lack of grace in dealing with it."

The whole crowd of a hundred and sixty-something people grew ever more quiet the longer Sarah spoke about John. Ever so often, the sniff that was a leftover of a mute tear would attempt to break the silence, but slowly fade; unheard. It was the first time Sarah was speaking publicly about her brother since he died, I had learned a lot about him the past few years, I think she talked to me most about him, maybe because I asked often, or maybe it's because I reminded her of him. His absence was one of the few things that made her sad.

He was quite the guy, from her account and those of people he knew and I had met. A lot of times, it felt like I had met him myself. Somehow he always made his way into every conversation at every dinner, every party, and every picnic where people who knew him were gathered; it was as if he was a wonder that refused to cease even after his death.

"We all lost John, three years ago, today," Sarah continued, as she adjusted the mouthpiece that sent her voice across the chapel. "For some of us, the void he left behind has been filled by someone or something else worthy of him, for others, he is immortalised in our hearts as a man that knew how to make us better.

Even as children, I could tell, I was only ever my best self when I had his approval. It's funny; he was the younger twin, but he was somehow so much better at living than I was. I knew it, but never resented him for it- he wielded his wisdom with humility and comic glee. In more ways than I can imagine, I became half of a piece of a puzzle after he died. Sometimes I look at my parents and our friends, and even at strangers I see on the streets or on the train and notice that they did too. John was the kind of person who made things complete.

John firmly believed that no one deserved to be forgotten. He always told me that it didn't matter how uninteresting, or how crazy I thought people were; no one was made to be forgotten. He convinced me that if I was patient enough to look closely at what I thought was their chaos; I'd always find the harmony between the smooth in their skin and the sharp in their edges that make them an infinite wonder.

He always wondered why it's so easy to find the faults and virtues of others, and remain blind to ours. All his life he walked around like a mirror; a non-judgmental instrument that showed us all our beautiful parts, and helped us conceal all the parts us we weren't proud of. He believed our fate as humans as to be imperfect, yet irreplaceable. He was the kind of person that saw the best in people. And looking at this room today, what he saw in all of us was the closest thing to the truth of the people we were growing to become.

I really don't want to take too much of your time today, telling you about what John meant to me. I'm trying not to cry. His was a life too well lived to mourn. I'm sure people have more pleasant things to say about him, some more beautiful and more surprising than those I could ever share.

Let's share those stories and let the tears that flow from our faces be from too much laughter.

I just came up here to say 'thank you,' to those of you that loved John enough not to forget him today, and on the other days that are his to be remembered by.

May we all live long;
May we all live in the hearts of the people that take our breath away,
and may they live in ours as well."

FISSURES IN HOPE

Her father always told her that the mountains we climb in life would often cliff into the sea, and it's then we must decide to either brave the unknown tides or draw back into our depressed valleys.

Nothing was more difficult for Sarah than having to believe she could still achieve her dreams without John. They had both shared similar ideas of how they wanted to fix a piece of our broken world. They had both tried when they were younger, and they had both failed. But because they had each other, they bore each other's burden of failures; the way siblings often do.

But Sarah had a will that defied gravity and the kind of eternal optimism that lit up the stars. "No one needs a reason to believe in themselves," she'd often say... "No one needs a reason to believe they are worthy of love or a second chance at happiness, despite their many failures... We simply believe because it's the only way to stop what's left of our fragile hearts from shattering into a million pieces - too broken to be put together again."

She never denied that life had broken her in some way; she took great pride in the faults in her soul and the fissures in the hope she still wielded as a shield. Whenever she spoke to me of her failed dreams, that's when she'd seldom reveal the scars that proved that sometime in her life she had fought for someone and lost, sometime in her life she tried to be something more than human, sometime in her life she had jumped off the cliff, and missed the quiet seas.

Still, that never stopped her.

She struggled at first, but she learned to believe in dreams again.

When we met, I could tell she was the girl who sought love as a distraction from the things she had lost, but she had now grown to become so much more. People grow, even the best people become better; we just have to let them.

There was something about her these days; she had finally found the courage to go the distance alone- without John. She became a different kind of Sarah: still as lovable, and mysterious as ever, but now she had rekindled a certainty in what she believed was her life's purpose.

"I've watched you get your dreams despite the odds and the failures," She said to me as we got ready for bed. "Somewhere in watching you, the desire to fight for mine became greater than the comfort of being afraid of failing again. It grew stronger than the convenience of not trying one more time. It became too real to be ignored, as it should be."

These days she barely slept for more than two hours at a stretch, even on nights when she stayed up really late painting or taking shots in the studio. Often, she'd wake up with an idea that kept her up the rest of the night, or a task in mind that had to be completed to prepare for her big gallery launch. We were both very busy with our dreams, but never too busy to sleep in the same bed.

Half asleep, I felt the duvet pull off me again. I was certain it was one of those times when she got up to do some work, and the draft of the cold air left by her empty bedside would hit me. She knew that always woke me up, even for a bit. I have a body made for warmth and cuddles. Something was different this time. Usually, the cold air stopped a few seconds after she let the duvet fall back in its place. It didn't this time. This time, the coolness was getting uncomfortably familiar, I was completely waking up. She had pulled the entire duvet off me.

I opened my eyes to find her sitting next to me in the grey lace
nightdress she often wore on the nights that were either too hot
she needed some air, or too cold she needed some of my
warmth. I looked at her. The sight of her thighs is the epiphany
that always reveals all my repressed longings. She is a queen
with a honeycomb that drips between her thighs.

We looked at each other, and we knew that loving was the
task we had both left undone for too long. Her desire for me
was audible in every breath she took; my longing for her grew
much longer. She kissed me with a kiss that reminds me why
her face could be a very sensual thing.

My tentacles reached for every part of her body; her hands
reached for every part of mine. My wet tongue *passioned* its
way from her lips to her chin - to the other parts of her that
always loved its caress. Her body wasn't the type that made it
difficult to please. She had these sister birthmarks on her left
nipple that made her body shriek whenever my tongue wetted,
and my lips pinched.

We misused our entire bodies, and confidently abused every
sturdy piece of furniture in our bedroom. We had long left the
normalcy of the bed behind; her face and the muffled sound of
my name were now deeply burrowed into the love seat we often
had our devotions in, and I was completely burrowed in her:
tunnelling my way through to our shared ecstasy.

She's about to blow.
I could always tell by how her moans fluttered erratically like
the Brownian in a wave right before it crashes passionately into
the sand.

I was too.

We both did.
Then we did again.

We never went back to bed on nights like this. We just held each other till the sun rose. And in the morning, she always became a perfect storm: my rare, dark and wet excuse to stay under the sheets.

Success is like an orgasm.
You always know when it's coming.

From Sean
To Sarah

Index Fingers

"Hey baby," she said, with her eye still looking through her camera, one hand holding the camera in place, the other waving at me. I seldom visited her at her studio, and even when I did, I barely got to speak to her. All day she'd hide behind camera lenses, capturing memories others didn't want to forget; as if she herself wasn't a miracle worth a billion unforgettable pixels.

I always enjoyed watching her work. It was the way she dealt with people that marvelled me the most. She turned the rules of human engagement on their heads. When she took portraits of adults, she treated them like children - not in a condescending way, but in an "I think you're an endless wonder filled with infinite potential way." And when she took portraits of children she made them believe every word that came out of their mouths had the power to create a constellation of beautiful tomorrows. You could see it in the portraits she took, every one of her images captured the people they were and the people they could one day become.

"Baby, How about a portrait?" She asked me as her model made his way out of the camera's focus and out of the studio. I could tell she was up to something; she wanted to get on my good side. We had argued earlier that morning about one of those things couples know they shouldn't really be arguing about, but still do anyways - those type of arguments that you can't put a 'why?' to a few years later.

"Okay," I said, without the slightest sign of excitement in my reply. I tend to be a man of very few words when patiently waiting for an apology.

My boresome response did nothing to sway her in the slightest - she was a woman with a plan. She just smiled and went about setting up the tripod to the perfect height, manoeuvring my stubborn body into the right position for the portrait. She skipped back to her camera, fiddled with it, and began with some tests shots. "Come on, baby, smile for the camera," she said repeatedly; completely ignoring my dispassionate exterior. She continued to fiddle with her camera, then stopped. She left it on the tripod, slowly walked behind me, wrapped herself around me and whispered "I said, smile for the camera, baby," as she gently prodded both her index fingers into my ribs, causing me to spasm in laughter. The camera flashes.

That portrait hangs tall in her gallery as a testament to her creative mischief and her uncanny ability to always make me happy. Underneath it are the words: "A tickle is an infinite amount of *I'm sorrys* at the tip of your fingers."

AWARD NIGHT.

She spreads herself agape on my desk.
"We're gonna be Late."

...

My fingers part the tides in her beige silk dress,
to find her completely
uninterested in decency.

A MARITAL TRYST

Husband:
"Forget everything else, the past is dead, the future is fleeting,
now is forever- this moment when love and lust are merged into
one fiery marital tryst is all the eternity we may ever get.

We are alone. Come closer. Reveal to my aching palms the
warmth hidden in the low of your back. You know where my
heart is, and where my lips would be: close your eyes and kiss
me.

This is Eden - no shame in nakedness. *Unfig* your body slowly
and make my words your only covering - imagine my eyes
gazing on your body, and you will feel my stare in your thighs.

Tonight I'm your potter, in my hands, you are moist clay. First,
I will make your earth quake, then make you shiver in the
showers of your rain; until this silent night has its drunken fill
of the cocktail of your moans."

Wife:
"I'm tired, let's do all that tomorrow."

CAMPFIRES

Do you remember the first night?
Two hearts tucked under one cover.
The pleasant discomfort of the cold;
Winter, peeping through our keyhole.

...

I became your campfire
and you became mine.

From Sarah
To Sean

RITUALS

We'd drive down to the place where we first kissed years ago;
we'd lie side by side on the open green field. We'd talk, we'd
laugh; we'd bask in the romantics of bright stars and dancing
fireflies.

All night we'd relish the past and dream of the future. Whether
we held hands or kissed, it didn't matter much. The magic of it
was in how nostalgia and faith meddled into one - how our past
and future seem to come alive in that moment.

Then after we had laughed at every memory, and revelled in
every dream that our beating hearts could muster, we'd sit
quietly, watching pilgrim clouds steal their way into promised
lands under the cover of the night sky.

And when the sun rose, we'd make our way back home,
convinced our hearts were filled with a year's worth of love.

...

This was the custom, on the eve of our wedding anniversary.

The Perfect Morning

Everything is still, the room is as quiet as darkness. The only
things that dared move are the living sculptures our shadows
mount on the rumpled linen beddings. I'm wide awake, I have
been for a while. My eyes worship every curve of her temple,
watching the sun caresses her skin with the warmth of
glistening honey.

She is beautiful as she sleeps curled up in an irresistible
invitation to cuddle. Auburn waterfalls gallop indiscriminately
from her head down to our pillows. She breathes ever so gently.
I only take my breaths when I'm sure she has taken hers- I'm
dead without her.

Her lips are the polar opposites of mine; I reach for the kind of
kiss that says both hello and goodbye all at once. She always
tastes like the sea; sweet, with a hint of earthy saltiness. She's
awake now; I know by how our magnets constantly collide. The
ambient silence of our suburban home slowly unravels into a
melange of expectant breathing and vibrations at pre-orgasmic
frequencies.

She pauses... too quickly to think abrupt, catches my eye for
less than a moment and dashes out of the room like a wild
gazelle desperate to outrun the arc of my hunting spear.

...

"It's been seven minutes, where is she?" Her fragrance travels at
the speed of thought. There is a mystery about her that fills
every room with the faint scent of Jasmine leaves whenever I
think of her. She walks back towards the room in steps of two,
paired with an awkward silence that lasts only as long as I
could hold my breath. She stops and leans carelessly on the

door frame, her face flushed, her fingers nervously plucking the strings of an invisible guitar, her eyes are dead fixed on me, but her thoughts are somewhere in the wind.

"What's going on honey?" I ask...

"I think I am pregnant," she mumbles...

Broken Resolve

We are rarely proud of the things we do to survive because very often it costs us the part of our souls that we should never lose: our dignity, our faith, our pride, our shame. You see, once we lose those parts of us to surviving, we rarely find them back - from then on we are slaves to it; we live and breathe for it. We do everything we must and more, in the name of survival.

I once met a beggar who struggled with this truth. You could tell he was new to the nuances of provoking pity, partly because he still felt pity for himself. He still struggled to let go of the shame that survival demanded he gave up. He still held on to his dignity. I looked at him and fondly remembered those days when all I had to fill my pockets were the fears of monthly bills, the remnants of a failed start-up, and some loose change.

He had timidly walked up to me and asked if he could get a few pounds to buy a meal. I nodded yes, but before I had completed my nostalgic thought and reached for my wallet, he had walked off; his feet briskly propelled by something in his conscience.

I watched him walk away and wished I could have told him that I once lived with the same uncertainties of where the hands that could feed me were. I wish I could have said to him that I was sorry life had thrown the weight I tossed aside on his back. I wish I had told him not to give in to the fleeting whims of survival- but to keep fighting to keep his shame, because sometimes that shame is what keeps our dreams alive. I hoped I had not seemed as cruel to look down on him at the moment where he needed me to strengthen his pride. I wished he could hear my thoughts...

Now, I see him often on the streets, begging and unashamed, and hope to God that I am not the constant reminder of the day life broke his resolve.

...

Driving past him today felt a bit more symbolic; I was heading to Nigeria to give a speech to a group of young entrepreneurs. I had not written down my speech, I rarely did. I trusted my heart to always know what to say in these situations like it does in most. I would talk about survival and hope and purpose, - it's all I know to talk about. Etim organised the event. He was now the head of one of the most successful private education systems in the whole of Nigeria - the perfect use of his diverse mind. He had become obsessed with giving back after our near brush with death in Paris 9 years ago[10]; I think the brevity of life is what drives him - it's what drives me too, sometimes.

I was the happiest I had ever been in my life. Sarah was pregnant with twins, my parents lived to see their son grow into a very successful business man, I got to watch them both age gracefully in time and pride. All was well with the world. Sarah was home working on a new exhibition: expectation always inspired her, and children are the ultimate expectation. This was one of the few times we couldn't travel together during our marriage. I always hated leaving her alone, but Etim called, and when friends like Etim call, you answer. More-so, it was always fun catching up with the old crew and laughing with their families too.

I thought some more on the Jet, about that beggar, and about how I could have helped if I had the confidence or common sense to speak to him. It was one of the things I think I most regret: having no words where words were needed. That made me think about Sarah, and about how our words to each other were what held us together through all of our lives, especially

---

[10] All of Paris in the Summer. Pg. 33

when we had to persist through what was our inexplicable inability to have any children. The children in her womb were as much a medical miracle as they were a divine one. I reached for my briefcase and brought out my journal; the one where I write to Sarah as often as I can. I had burned through seven of those journals already; Sarah was on her eighth.
I put my pen to the page and looked outside the window to the clouds; they always hid raindrops and fine words - and I wanted to fill the page with poetry. Writing poems and letters to Sarah was how I sent her little pieces of my heart.

I started to write, and the plane began to shake. It was one of those unexpected turbulences again. I rested back into the sofa, waiting for it to stop. It did, so did my worrisome thoughts. No matter how many times you fly, turbulences are never welcome. I attempted writing again, soon after we hit another bout of turbulence, this one worse than the first- we were losing altitude fast- in fact, it felt like we no longer in the air, but were running through an earthquake and a tornado.

Finally, everything got steady; the worried look on my personal assistant's face leaves, I'm not sure mine did. Mike, our pilot, spoke through the onboard public address system, explaining what happened. There is always a confidence in his voice that puts my fear of flying to rest. He advised us to sit tight with our seat belts fastened for the rest of the flight. I did as he asked.

We landed in Lagos safely. Etim's wife Claudia and his two daughters Idara, and Aniedi were waiting for me by a black Mercedes on the tarmac. "Uncle Segun, Uncle Segun!" they shouted as they ran towards me. They knew me by my native Nigerian name; Olusegun, not the Sean I had bestowed upon myself when I moved to the UK. "I hear Sarah is heavy with the twins," Claudia said with a sunny grin on her face.

"Yeah, she is, she's due in about two weeks, but I'm sure you know that. She'd have loved to be here, but the doctors advised us she shouldn't fly." They were always fond of Sarah. One of my favourite memories was of her, Sarah and the two girls playing soccer that one time we all went on vacation together. All their feet always seemed to miss the ball except for Idara's; she was a natural at sports. I remember watching Sarah with the girls; it made me want children so badly.

We drove down to the chopper and made our way straight to the conference. I had come in specifically for the conference and was going to head back to Manchester once I finished my speech. Sarah was already miles in minutes away from me, and like petals plucked from a rose, I wither when we're apart.

We arrived at the conference centre in about fifteen minutes; it was being held at one of these new hotels on Lagos Island. As I looked down at the endless queue of cars and buses from our helicopter, I remember how long it usually took us to drive down from the airport to the island when I was growing up. "Traffic in Lagos always makes you late for all the things you can't afford to be late for, even now that the city is much developed," Claudia said, shaking her head we landed.

Etim was as close to the helipad as he could be without risking his life. Caution was his best friend. I could see him as we landed. He had aged, he now sported a full beard, and his head was balding gracefully. He still fiddled curiously with his glasses the same way he always did back in school when his mind was fixed on solving a problem.

"You're up to speak next," he said as he gave me our customary bro hug. "We'd catch up after your talk." Whenever there was a task at hand, it always had his complete attention.

"Oh, okay,"

I walked into the conference room just as I was being introduced, and headed straight for the stage. I had imagined it would be a room of maybe 500 people; it wasn't. There were about 5000 people seated in that huge room. I looked at the faces in the crowd. I saw some familiar faces and many unfamiliar ones. That whole room was electrified with so many dreams and infinite possibilities that it started to fill my heart with words just as I expected it would.

I got up the stage and immediately started to speak.

"I'm not sure how many of you in the room know this, but before there were digital cameras in phones that took photographs you could print in an instant, photographers had to take pictures and print them through a very tedious process. In that process, the photographers had to begin with miniature samples of the pictures they had taken; those miniature samples were called negatives. The negatives always looked nothing like the image they had captured, but they were vital to getting the final physical print. They'd take these negatives to the darkroom, and it's in the darkness they'd turn the negatives into the final prints.

Entrepreneurship makes us all like those photographers, and she does it like this. First, she inspires you not to accept the status-quo by giving you a dream: an image of an irresistible future, or maybe an idea: you all have one of those, I can see it in your eyes, I can feel it in the air. It's as vivid, and as clear to you as every other thing you can see or touch. It's a piece of your life's purpose.

You see, by inspiring you not to accept the status-quo she teaches you the very valuable art of 'not accepting,' - that makes you a non-conformist, a radical. In a way, we are all conformists, but some of us conform only to the patterns of non-conformity, never accepting things as they are, but imagining them as they could be. That's the first sign you're an entrepreneur.

But the thing about non-conformity is that it separates you from everything and everyone in order to reintroduce you to yourself. It sends you on the lonesome journey of self-discovery.

Armed with the skill of non-conformity, self-identity and a heart filled with passion you start chasing your dreams. You start trying to make the dream a physical reality. Usually what happens is that you'd first hit a road block - a failure. The first thing you should expect when chasing a dream is disappointment. I'm not saying that's always true, but be prepared for it.

What happens more often than not is that life begins to throw at you the negatives of the very image you have dreamed; loneliness, fear, failure, rejection, loss, debt - she would throw them at you in quick succession- take it!

But entrepreneurship requires that you not fall under them or accept them, or let them frame your identity. What she expects is that you learn to hold on to hope in spite of them. That's the kind of hope that allows you work with the negatives... That's what faith is, working with your negatives, seeing the possibilities in failure, and working to make those possibilities real. Your dreams will never become a reality until your failures become opportunities. Like those photographers, it is in working with our negatives that you can turn those images we carry in our minds into physical reality. Entrepreneurship requires that you embrace the negatives!

Nothing great was ever created in your comfort zone!

Growing up, my father always said: "We are all convicts of our minds - the difference is some of us build palaces that allow us

run free, while others build prisons that hold them bound."
Seated in this room are palace builders, day dreamers, and free
runners. I dare you all to dream as big as you can, and run as
fast as you can.

A word of caution though, there will be times in your life when
you will hit a crossroads of sort. It would be a time when all
your dreams would have failed; when the negatives of life have
overwhelmed you. It would be a trying time- it will be a very
dark time for you, but just like photographers; it's only in the
darkness you can turn your negatives into positives.

Typically, in those times, you'd have two types of choices that
face you - you'd either have to do things to keep your dream
alive, or do things just to survive the day to day and let go
of the negatives that surround you. Choose to keep your
dreams alive; embrace the negatives. Never do things for the
sole purpose of survival. Survival traps you in a loop; it makes
you slave to the idea of it. Survival would demand that you let
go of your pride, your shame, your faith, and then ultimately
your dreams. It will slowly replace your dreams with the
overwhelming need to get by day to day, slowly changing the
architecture of your minds; turning your palaces of infinite
possibilities into prisons of self-doubt and self-loathing. It kills
the drive in you, without which you may not live to fight
another day. Fight now; fight long; fight till the end.

It's inescapable; your heart will break when dreams seem to
fail, but hold on to hope, stay optimistic in the face of trying
times; believe in yourself and always desire the impossible.
Everyone deserves an impossible story- everyone deserves a God
story! I've had a few of those in my life.

Your dreams stand the greatest chance of becoming real if you
chase them wholeheartedly.

It's unwavering belief that keeps our heart whole in trying times.

It takes a whole heart to see possibilities, to persist, to really really dream, and to press on despite challenges.

Faith and persistence are two sides of the exact same coin. It doesn't matter which side you turn up to pay the price for your dreams, the value of the coin stays the same. Faith and persistence will always make impossible things happen.

Above all, in your pursuit of dreams, be good. Respect your word and most importantly, respect people. Every soul is an impossible number of miracles waiting to happen.

Don't be deceived by the glitz and glamour, even the best of us are lost in some way; and no matter how perfect our individual lives seem, we would always be lone pieces of a puzzle that have no real value until we come together. Many of you here in this room will lead great industries; some of you would change Nigeria, some of you; the world! But you cannot do it without respect for those whom you lead.

Every soul is an impossible number of miracles waiting to happen- it's your job as leaders to make those miracles happen.

The older I get, the more I see that maybe we were made to major in the minors; to keep human courtesy alive. Maybe it's not just about the great feats we achieve in industry or commerce, but in the little things we do to preserve our collective dignity as a race and the love we have for each other. Maybe our lives matter because of the number of people we've made smile, the dreams we've inspired, the broken hearts we've mended, and the fallen dreamers we've reminded how to fly.

Maybe it's about the number of steps we took walking in love in a world where all everyone does is fall.

Maybe that sums up why we've all really been placed here; to walk in love, to mend broken things, and to teach fallen angels how to fly. Maybe that's what success is all about.

There is a lot of work to be done, and for you, there are much brighter days ahead, but there are also many dark days - I'm sorry, but it's true. I'm here today not to make you afraid of the dark, but to light a fire of hope in your hearts. It's a fire that would guide you through the darkest of times; and no matter how dark your days get, I pray heaven would always paint you a glorious sunset.

Nothing lasts forever,
Except persistence
- that should last forever.
Persist!

Thank you and God bless all of you. "

. . .

I immediately got off the stage, said hi to a handful of colleagues and began to make my way out of the conference room. Etim and I walked out with a number of remarkable entrepreneurs he'd wanted me to meet. They were all inspiring and filled with potential. Some bore the scars of failure; those were the ones I found the most potential in.

After the meet and greet, Etim and I started to make our way back to the helipad. We chatted about something I honestly can't remember now. My phone rang, it was Sarah. I was unable to pick up, what we were discussing seemed really important at the time, too important to cut him short abruptly.
"I'd call her right back," I thought.

We spoke for another five minutes; then I reached for my phone to call Sarah. "Etim could I please get a glass of water; I'm feeling rather light headed." I started to feel disoriented and confused; unable to remember where I was, or why I was even there. I had been feeling light headed on and off for a while, but now breathing became a chore altogether and there was this sharp pain in my chest I could no longer ignore. I struggled to stay standing by holding on to things I could find closest to me but finally gave in to gravity. I fell to the ground and passed out, long before they could get the glass of water to me.

ANATOMY OF A BROKEN HEART

I wake up some hours later at home. Not home in Manchester with Sarah, but home in Dad's hospital in Lagos; the place where my childhood memories were made of. Jide, my big brother, walks into the room. He took over the hospital after Dad and Mom retired and moved to Abuja, and he's done a great job growing it into something much more remarkable than the masterpiece Dad handed him. He has the same look on his face he always had when he got a scolding from mom those days when we were growing up. I never liked seeing him like that.

"You didn't even tell me you'd be in town, Segun."

"I only intended to come in for about an hour and head back. I didn't think it would be necessary - tell me Jide, is it bad news?"

"How are you feeling, Segun?" He always avoided questions with questions.

"Still a little sore in my chest and drowsy as well..."

"Okay, that's expected, it's the meds that are making you drowsy. You passed out at the conference centre. Your friend Etim actually called me and airlifted you here; he only left a few minutes ago when you were stable. You're lucky a helicopter was standing by, and a friend that was ready to move the earth for you. That was a coincidence that probably saved your life. We carried out some MRI's chest X-rays and ECGs while you were semi-conscious, and found out you have an Atrial septal defect: it's a congenital heart anomaly.

It's basically a hole in your heart you've carried around from birth. It's very easy to spot these days but unfortunately for you, at the time you were born, it wasn't that easy to diagnose in Nigeria. It's no fault of yours, many babies who are born with atrial septal defects show no symptoms until middle age or much later. Unfortunately, we're just catching yours."

"So the happiest man in the world could die of a broken heart," I thought.

"I already flew in our cardiothoracic expert Dr. Kennogbon for a consult. He suggests immediate open heart surgery would be your best bet. There would have been some less invasive options, but the hole in your heart has grown larger over the years, and he thinks we'd have to get in there to fix it- open heart surgery is your best option. He'd come to talk to you through it soon. I'm here first because I feel you needed to hear this from me. Honestly, I'm here because you're my little bro, and you definitely need a friendly face right now. You know I can't be in the operating room with you, but I'd be watching throughout, and Dr. Kennogbon is one of the best in Africa, so you're in good hands."

"Okay, thanks, Jide. Is that the doctor standing by the window?"

Jide looks at the window, and looks back at me, half confused, "There is no one at the window, Segun."

The man by the window turns to look at me. I immediately recognise his face. It's the strange man from the train again. Why is he here?

Jide continues to talk about my diagnosis and surgery. He was not moved by the fact that he didn't see anyone by the window. Sometimes I joked like that. I'd tell him something was somewhere and laugh at him when he looked and it wasn't. This wasn't one of those times, but he didn't know that.

"I have to let you know that the surgery is high risk for someone your age. I've called Sarah to fill her in. Unfortunately, I don't advise she travels in her condition as well, and even if she did, you'd be in surgery by the time she arrives. We have to get you into surgery immediately and hope for the best.

It's a miracle you've lived this long, but your life has been one medical miracle after another since you were born, I'm expecting you'd pull one more miracle out of your ass for Sarah and the babies."

Jide knew a lot more about all the many impossibilities I had faced in my life than anyone. He knew how I was born 2 months premature and had to fight to live. He knew how I had recovered from a diagnosis of irreparable nerve damage to my left leg when I was 13; he was there through all of it.

Having him here for this gave me much confidence. But seeing the man from the train in the room was very unsettling. All I could remember was him telling me he had been with people when they were filled with life and when they were close to death. Which one was it this time?

"Where is my phone? I need to call Sarah, and please pass me the journal in my briefcase too." He hands me the things I asked for and walks out to give me some privacy.

The phone rings once, and Sarah picks it. "Segun how are you?"

She's trying to sound calm, but I know she only calls me Segun when she's worried, upset or afraid.

"I'm fine baby; Jide says he's filled you in, I'll be going in for surgery soon. How are the twins? Hope they are not kicking too hard?"

"They are fine, waiting for their dad to come back home. Come back to us Segun, don't you dare leave me alone! You know I want to be there with you right now- I hate that I can't."

"I know baby, and you know I'll never leave you alone. As long as you breathe, so will I."

"You better!"

We continued to talk and find solace in how much we knew we still needed each other, then I decide to tell her what was really on my mind.

"Uh, Sarah,"

"Yes?"

"That man is here again,"

"What man?"

"The man from the train, the one I told you I saw or had a dream of on the same day I met you."

She pauses... I know what she's thinking, I know I just made her more afraid. No one wants to hear their loved ones are seeing invisible beings when they're going into surgery.

"What's he doing, or saying?"

"Nothing, he's just standing by the window looking at the trees."

"Hmm. You said the last time he came he brought hope, didn't he, maybe that's why he's here again — to bring you hope."

I knew she remembered the fact that the strange man had told her had been with people close to their deaths, but she'd never say it. She was never one to give voice to her fears.

"Yes honey, hope... I'm going to get wheeled in for surgery soon, and I need to call my folks. I think I have to get off the line now..."

"Okay.
Come back to me Segun; fight like hell if you must, but make sure you come back to me. I need you like the moon needs the Sun!"

"I will baby, I Love you."

"I love you too..."

We both stay on for a while saying nothing, yet reluctant to hang up- we always found comfort in each other's silence. Neither of us could attempt to say "bye"- that's a very dangerous thing to say at times like these.

Soon after, the line breaks....
I reach for my journal. "I need to write something to Sarah and the twins, just in case.[11]" The strange man is still standing by the window with his hands in his pockets, looking outside at the trees.

...

I finish writing just as Jide and Dr. Kennogbon walk in. He is dressed in blue cotton theatre scrubs. He introduces himself

---

[11] The promise of something divine. Pg. 108; Daughter, on your journey, Pg. 110; Son, on your journey. Pg. 112; In the chasing of dreams, Pg. 114 & If all that was left, Pg. 116.

and goes over the procedure in more detail – explaining the anatomy of my broken heart, and how he is going to fix it. I pretend to be listening, all the while wondering why the strange man was here, and why he hadn't said anything to me.

"Whenever you're ready, the anaesthetist will come in to sedate you. Have you spoken to Sarah?" Jide asks.

"Yeah I have."

"Mom, and dad?"
"I Called them right after I spoke to Sarah."

"Okay good, are you ready to go in for surgery?" Jide asks again, with a bit of concern in his voice.

"As ready as I will ever be."

He says a prayer for me and signals for the anaesthetist. She comes in almost immediately with some medical gadgetry in her hands, sets it up, and inserts a needle in my left arm. As I begin to fall into my medically induced coma, the strange man walks towards me, bends over and says;

"Come with me; It's time I show you how beautiful Heaven is."

What comes next are the words Sean *(Segun)* wrote to Sarah and his unborn twins right before he went into surgery.

THE PROMISE OF SOMETHING DIVINE

My father, your grandfather, wrote to us every day. He didn't do it much when we were very young, but I think sometime in his life he learned the power of words, and how they were the vessels of affection and guidance. I think he learned the power of a single verse to shape a whole life.

In his many letters, he taught us to dream and cautioned us that every dreamer must learn to know sorrow and love hope. He taught us to keep optimism in the face of tests; he was a Medical Doctor, but it was his words that did the healing of our souls.

He reminded us often of how his life was a humdrum pursuit of nothingness until he realised that our destinies were not hidden in stars beyond our reach, but were revealed in the beautiful things our hands could make, the broken dreams our hearts still believed, and the pain our souls were brave enough to share.

He taught us not to look to past failures because nothing destroys imagination like regret. He taught us to trust wholeheartedly in God. He taught us empathy for our leaders and patience; he taught us always to remember, that only ships unbroken by storms, can voyage home - and so we must not let life break us. He taught us to love, and to do it with the kind of calm that makes the deer trust in gentle streams.

I have seen that my life is merely a shadow of the words I've believed. I've seen how my life changed because I was unafraid to be guided by a well-written verse. I've seen dark days become bright by the light in words. And I have seen how words can be the lifeblood of a great love. It's why I'm leaving you with words.

I'm writing these letters to you unsure if these are the only words you'll ever get from me. Yet I'm ashamed I have no better lessons to hand to you on how to live your life than the same ones I learned from my father. As it seems to me lying on this hospital bed, ready to be wheeled in for surgery, life could have chosen to rob me of the opportunity to hear your laughter; but like your mother's, I know it will sound like the promise of something divine.

I love you.
Dad.

DAUGHTER, ON YOUR JOURNEY

I have yet to meet you,
I have yet to tell your mother,
that you are the one thing I've found holds more wonder than
she...
And you, you have yet to bring joyful tears to my eyes.
Yet, I have these words to share,
as you begin love's Journey,

My sweet daughter,

Always smile, dear one,
because affection smiles:

Laughter and tears,
both frighten your fears,
laughter and tears,
both disarm the armour a man bears;

yet, I'd rather you laughed always,
because it is better for your heart.

Keep your temple, dear one,
and give your heart with care.
Know that hearts can be broken
and hearts are to be earned.

So love one man,
but prove his worth first.

If best of friends fight for your affection,
do not choose one for the other.
Because if you do,
you will three hearts, break.

Honesty is better than chivalry,
but the two together will a godly man yield.
So give a godly man your heart,
and he will forever keep it.

Never toy with a man's heart,
it is more fragile than you know.

So, Love first,
and love last.

Real love fixes everything
because it quits at nothing.
So love patiently, my dear,
love patiently like your mother.

Do not want the affections of a short tempered man;
when you leave him, you incur his wrath.

Give any man a reason to doubt your love,
and you may forever lose him to doubt.

Know that Beauty is divine,
but more divine is a faithful woman.
So, be faithful, my dear,
because virtue is greater than lust.

Above all,
love God, with passion,
and with passion shall you be loved.

From your Dad.

Son, On your Journey

Although, I am yet to be a father to you.
And you are yet to bring me unspeakable Joy.
Although, I'm unsure I'd ever hear your cries,
or ever get to make you laugh.

I have written these words to you,
in hopes, that they would guide your days,
and give you rest at night.

My Dear Son,

Always give more than you receive,
even in an uncertain affection.

Love only one woman,
but leave if she loves another.
Because it is better to lose your love,
than to forever want hers.

Son, do not fight for a woman's affections,
hearts are not won; they are earned.
So, make yourself worthy of her,
and she will freely give you her heart.

Never despise a lost love,
when you do, you reveal your broken heart.

Know that the right woman will take all of your heart,
so be prepared to guard all of hers.

Your heart is your soul's rudder,
be careful, lest you lose your way.
Remember, your heart has only one voice;
listen always to its drumming.

A beast is made a man by the woman he loves.
A man is made a beast by the woman he loves.
So, love a godly woman,
and she will your innocence, preserve.

Never love a mocker,
lest you become the thing of her tales.

Do not play with a woman's heart,
if you break it, it will pierce you.

Hold on tightly to your love
only as long as she wants to be held.
Learn always to leave when you must,
and stay when she wills.

Be careful my boy, not to get your heart broken,
but be more careful not to break any.
With this in mind, be faithful;
because a man who breaks his vow is worse than a thief.

Above all,
Love God with everything you have.
To him, your love is worth everything

With love- Dad

In the Chasing of Dreams.

My children,

There is great nobility
first, in the chasing of love,
and second,
in the chasing of a dream.

Do both!
but in doing these,
never despise rationality,
but learn to dream with reckless abandon,
and plan with frugal intricacy.

Know that in the pursuit of dreams,
there is always a pessimist
and also an optimist.
Sometimes you are both.
Sometimes you're none.
But if you could choose one
be the second,
and be the one who always hopes
on everyone's accord.

Teach everyone,
whether their cups
are half empty,
or half full,
that sometimes,
you need to turn
things up-side-down-wards
to make them work.

So, guard your heart, diligently
And with it, guard your head.

Let your recklessness protect your cares.
Let your generosity guard your thrift.
Hide all your doubts in hope.
Love always, even when it is folly to do so.
Learn to be wise, but sometimes act a fool...

Your heart beats for a reason,
to remind you
it's there for your using-
-use it!
In matters of speaking,
of thinking
and decision making.

Because although a choice by the heart
might seem wrong to the head,
but a choice made by the head
might just break your heart;
and a broken heart
breeds a fruitless mind, doesn't it?

So in the chasing of dreams,
like in the chasing of love;
do right by your heart always,
and let your head follow.
It will...
It always does...
When you leave it
with no other choice.

IF ALL THAT WAS LEFT.

If all that was left
of my time
was a breath,
with it
I'll blow you
an eternal kiss.

If all that was left
of my heart
was a beat,
I will gladly
let it skip
at one more
sight of you.

If all that was left
of all beauty
was one smile,
It would be yours
my dear,
It will be yours!

If all that was left
of all magic
was a wish,
I'd ask
for one more
eternity
with you.

If all that was left
of my poetry
was one,
I hope
It's this ode

I write
to you.

From Sean
To Sarah

Heaven is waking up to the sound of your yawns every morning

I'm coming back to you, baby.

The End.
Thanks for reading.

As shadows forever long for flesh and bone, our souls will always lust for a kind of affection that's completely beyond us. It's either our collective need for self-actualization or self-destruction- but it's the kind of love we are all designed to desire nonetheless.

It's the kind of love we all deserve.

And it's the kind of love I hope you find.

Sola,

It hurt to hear you died
on a sunny Sunday afternoon so bright
it made people forget all the evil in the world.

But like you always did when you were alive;
you left me with a whole lot of magic,
and the memory of a smile
that I could only capture with beautiful words.

Rest in Peace.

For God.

There was nothing in me,
until you put eternity
and sixteen billion infinities
in my soul.

Thank you.

Follow O.O.Kukoyi
For excerpts and updates on new books.

https://www.instagram.com/o.o.kukoyi/

OOKUKOYI.COM

Made in the USA
Charleston, SC
24 October 2016